the Golden Cockerel

And then the poor old King had a dreadful time! No sooner did he send an army to the North, than the Magician's armies would attack from the South. And when Dadon sent his warriors to the East, the enemy would surely come from the West. So the King's armies never got a chance to fight the mysterious foe.

WILLY POGÁNY—

All these troubles kept the King from taking his nice long naps in the huge feather bed, and he didn't like this at all! So he called a meeting of his wise men, the boyars. He was sure they could tell him from which direction the enemy would come.

The boyars sat before the King and thought day and night over this mighty problem. After many days and many nights, they finally decided that the only one who could help the King was the fortune teller. So old Dadon commanded that the fortune teller come quickly. But the boyars shook their heads at this order, and then the eldest and wisest arose with great dignity. He stroked his long, grey beard and said, "But, mighty Dadon, the fortune teller has been dead for many, many years."

This bad news made the King very unhappy. Then all the wise men began to talk at once.

"If our fortune teller were alive," said one of them, "he could save our kingdom with his magic mixture of beans, cooked in a large iron pot with a strange and secret herb."

"Beans!" said another boyar. "Pooh! Who
ever heard such nonsense! Now I heard of a witch
who could foretell the future with grains of sand."

"Sand!" screeched another boyar. "How silly!
By the stars alone can one tell the future."

Soon the royal halls fairly shook with
"Beans" – "Sand" – "Piffle" – "Stars" – "Nonsense!"
as each boyar shouted as loudly as he could.

The King by this time was almost weeping with rage and disappointment. "Enough!" he shouted, pounding his sceptre on the floor, "Away with all of you! You have brought me no help in my hour of need."

The boyars had never before seen jolly old Dadon in such a temper. They looked at each other in surprise. They were deeply hurt at his ungratefulness. Were they not the wisest men in the kingdom? And had they not thought and thought for days and days to help him?

Just when all seemed black with despair, there suddenly appeared an old, old man, carrying a bundle under his arm. He approached the throne, bowed deeply before the King and said, "Hail, O mighty King! I knew well your great-great-grandfather, and his grandfather before him. Tales of your great distress have reached my ears and I have brought you a gift."

He reached in the bundle and brought forth a Golden Cockerel. "Take this bird, O Majesty!" he said, "Place him on a spire atop one of the turrets of your castle. He will watch over your kingdom. If all is well, he will sit peaceful and quiet. But if there be a sign of danger, of enemies advancing to

destroy and pillage your lands, then this Golden Cockerel will begin to crow:

> Cock-a-doodle-do!
> Awake! Arise! The foe's at hand!
> Seize your arms! Defend your land!
> Cock-a-doodle-do!

and he will flap his wings and turn to whence the danger is coming."

Now the King listened hopefully to the old man's story, without really believing a word of it. And all the wise men looked down their noses. But poor tired Dadon was willing to try anything.

He commanded that the bird be placed on the spire. To his great delight he found that the old man had spoken the truth, for the Golden Cockerel flapped his wings and crowed:

> Cock-a-doodle-do!
> All is peaceful,
> All is well.
> Cock-a-doodle-do!

The old King fairly bounced with happiness and glee. He even forgot that he was angry with the boyars.

"How can I ever thank you?" the King asked the old, old man. "Surely there is some wish of yours that I might grant. Name anything you choose and it shall be yours."

The old man bowed politely and said, "I will remember your promise." Then he left, and no sooner was he outside the palace gate than he began to cackle with laughter. "Ho! Ho! Ho!" he laughed, until he could hardly stop, for he was none other than the evil Magician of the Dark Mountains, disguised as a kindly old man. He was very, very pleased because at last he had found a way to trick the King.

Peacefully two years went by and the Golden Cockerel sat quietly on his spire. The old King spent his days feasting on rich and delicious foods and taking long naps on his huge feather bed.

And then there was great excitement in the kingdom, for the King's only son, the brave Prince Igor, had fallen in love with the beautiful Princess Tatiana. Splendid preparations were being made for their wedding and the people went about singing and laughing.

One afternoon, the King was taking his usual nap in his big feather bed. His court ladies, who had gathered around the bed to drive the flies away with their silken handkerchiefs, slowly, one by one, dropped off to sleep. Even the faithful housekeeper, Dunya, was at last overcome by drowsiness and put her red head down on the edge of the bed. The only sound to be heard was the loud snoring of the old King. His crown was tipped over his nose and on his face was a happy smile. He was dreaming a magnificent dream of mince pies and strawberry tarts and other good things to eat.

Suddenly, outside, the Golden Cockerel began to stir. Then, arching his neck and wildly flapping his wings, he crowed a mighty warning:

Cock-a-doodle-do!
Awake! Arise! The foe's at hand!
Seize your arms! Defend your land!
Cock-a-doodle-do!

and he pointed in the direction of the East.

The Golden Cockerel's warning was heard from one end of the land to the other. The people rushed here and there in fright, for they knew that great danger was upon them.

Inside the palace everyone seemed to be running up and down the stairs. The Generals were running about looking for their swords and helmets. The soldiers were looking for the Generals, and the court ladies were very busy packing baskets of good things to eat for their favorite warriors.

General Pushka rushed into the palace and found the old King still asleep. "Awake!" he shouted, shaking him. "Awake! Great danger threatens!!"

The King opened his eyes and yawned. "Who is it? What is it? Where?" he asked, still half asleep.

"The Golden Cockerel has warned us. You see, he is pointing to the East," explained the excited General. And at this moment the Cockerel crowed again, even more mightily than before:

Cock-a-doodle-do!
Awake! Arise! The foe's at hand!
Seize your arms! Defend your land!
Cock-a-doodle-do!

"The horrid thing," said the King, shaking his sleepy head. "Just as I was having the loveliest dream, too. However," he said with a deep sigh, "I suppose I must look after the affairs of State."

Then came the carriage with King Dadon and the beautiful Princess Shamaka. All the people cheered and waved their colored handkerchiefs, and the King stood up and bowed deeply to his loyal subjects.

Suddenly, out of nowhere, the wicked Magician appeared, again dressed as an old man. He wended his way through the crowd to the royal carriage. And looking at the beautiful Princess Shamaka, he said, "Great King, it is I, and I have come to get my reward for giving you the Golden Cockerel who brought you this good fortune."

"Welcome," answered the King. "Tell me of your wish and it shall be granted."

"King Dadon," the Magician went on, "I ask as my reward the beautiful Princess of the Moon."

"You must have lost your senses," shouted the King. He was terribly angry at this outrageous request. "Come! Come!" he said, "ask something reasonable and it shall be yours. But the Princess, never!"

"You promised," snarled the Magician. Then he laughed a very wicked laugh. "Do you know who I am? I will show you!" And with this, the old, old man vanished quick as a wink, and there stood the evil Magician of the Dark Mountains.

WILLY POGÁNY

"I'll teach you to break your promise!" he shrieked. "All my life I have wanted the Princess of the Moon. It was I who turned the man she loved into that Golden Cockerel. It was I who lured you to her country and bewitched her so that she was willing to come with you. For only if she is brought to me by a mortal can I have her." Once more he laughed his wicked laugh. He was very happy for he saw that everyone about him was feeling quite miserable.

And then, just as the evil Magician reached out to claim the Princess Shamaka, lo and behold! from the top of the spire the Golden Cockerel let out a mighty crow. Too late the Magician saw the bird swooping down at him. Before he could move to save himself, the Golden Cockerel had pecked him hard on the head. And the wicked ruler of the Dark Mountains dropped dead.

Then the Golden Cockerel flew over to the sad and beautiful Princess Tatiana and said, "Do not be so sad, O Princess! Now that this evil creature is no more I can help you. Pluck the golden

Number Theory and Fraction Concepts

Table of Contents

Letter Home iv
Pretest 1

Section A Factors and Multiples 3
Skill 1 Factors and Divisibility 4
Skill 2 Primes and Composites 5
Skill 3 Prime Factorization 6
Skill 4 Exponents 7
Skill 5 Prime Factorization with Exponents 8
Skill 6 Greatest Common Factor 9
Skill 7 Least Common Multiple 10
Skill 8 PROBLEM SOLVING: Draw a Diagram 11
         Test Prep and Mixed Review 12

Section B Introduction to Fractions 13
Skill 9   Writing a Fraction as Part of a Set or Part of a Whole 14
Skill 10 Estimating Fractional Amounts 15
Skill 11 Equivalent Fractions 16
Skill 12 Simplest Form 17
Skill 13 Writing Fractions with the Least Common Denominator 18
          Test Prep and Mixed Review 19

Section C Fractions, Mixed Numbers, and Decimals 20
Skill 14 Improper Fractions and Mixed Numbers 21
Skill 15 Improper Fractions, Quotients, and Mixed Numbers 22
Skill 16 Comparing and Ordering Fractions and Mixed Numbers 23
Skill 17 Writing Equivalent Fractions and Decimals 24
Skill 18 Dividing to Change a Fraction to a Decimal 25
          Test Prep and Mixed Review 26

Post-test A 27
Post-test B 29
Student Answer and Assignment Sheet 31
Answer Key and Correlation 32
Class Profile 33
Item Analysis 34
Easy-Score Answer Card .... —
Transparencies 1–8

Date _____

Dear _____,

    During the next few weeks, _____
will be working on lessons from the Number Theory and Fraction Concepts unit
of the Prentice Hall Skills Intervention Kit. The results of a recent pretest show
that your child would benefit from extra practice with certain skills relating to
number theory and fraction concepts. Throughout this unit, skills are presented
in a step-by-step manner to help your child achieve success.

    The Number Theory and Fraction Concepts Unit contains these three sections:

- ❑ *Section A: Factors amd Multiples*
  *This section contains eight lessons that review topics such as using
  prime and composite numbers, and finding factors and multiples.*
- ❑ *Section B: Introduction to Fractions*
  *This section contains five lessons that review topics such as writing
  fractions and finding equivalent fractions.*
- ❑ *Section C: Fractions, Mixed Numbers, and Decimals*
  *This section contains five lessons that review topics such as comparing
  fractions and mixed numbers and changing fractions to decimal form.*

    As always, your cooperation is requested to ensure that the assignments are
completed on time. If you have any questions regarding your child's work,
please send a note indicating your concerns, or phone me at
_____. Our combined support and encouragement will
help your child successfully complete this unit.

Sincerely,

Name _____   Date _____   Class _____

 PRETEST:
Number Theory and Fraction Concepts

Section A
Factors and Multiples

1. Which is *not* a factor of 48?

   A 4   **C** 12

   B 10   **D** 16

2. Which is a prime number?

   F 32   **H** 29

   G 65   **J** 57

3. Which is the prime factorization of 56?

   A $2 \times 2 \times 2 \times 7$

   B 4×14

   C 8×7

   D $2 \times 3 \times 3 \times 3$

4. Which is the standard form for 2^5?

   F 32   **H** 25

   G 10   **J** 52

5. Which is the prime factorization for 600 using exponents?

   A $2 \times 2 \times 2 \times 3 \times 5 \times 5$

   B $2 + 2 + 2 + 3 + 5 + 5$

   C $2^3 \times 3 \times 5^2$

   D $2^2 \times 33 \times 5^2$

6. Which is the greatest common factor of 36 and 54?

   F 12   **H** 6

   G 9   **J** 18

7. Which is the least common multiple of 24 and 36?

   A 12   **C** 60

   B 864   **D** 72

8. Water bottles are packed 8 per box. Energy snacks are packed 6 per box. If Jerome wants to buy the same number of water bottles as energy snacks, what is the least number of boxes of water bottles he can buy?

   F 2   **H** 6

   G 3   **J** 12

Section B
Introduction to Fractions

9. Which tells how much is shaded?

   A $\frac{5}{9}$ **C** $\frac{9}{9}$

   B $\frac{1}{9}$ **D** $\frac{4}{9}$

  Go On

10. Which tells about how much is shaded?

F $\frac{1}{2}$ H $\frac{1}{4}$

G $\frac{2}{3}$ J $\frac{3}{4}$

11. Which is equivalent to $\frac{2}{5}$?

A $\frac{2}{10}$ C $\frac{6}{10}$

B $\frac{8}{20}$ D $\frac{12}{35}$

12. Which is in simplest form?

F $\frac{9}{10}$ H $\frac{8}{12}$

G $\frac{4}{16}$ J $\frac{7}{14}$

13. Which shows equivalent fractions for $\frac{3}{4}$ and for $\frac{2}{3}$ using the least common denominator?

A $\frac{9}{12}$; $\frac{8}{12}$ C $\frac{6}{8}$; $\frac{4}{8}$

B $\frac{18}{24}$; $\frac{16}{24}$ D $\frac{3}{12}$; $\frac{2}{12}$

Section C
Fractions, Mixed Numbers, and Decimals

14. Which shows the improper fraction for $5\frac{4}{7}$?

F $\frac{16}{7}$ H $\frac{35}{7}$

G $\frac{39}{7}$ J $\frac{140}{7}$

15. Write $\frac{46}{9}$ as a whole or mixed number.

A 5   C $1\frac{5}{9}$

B $5\frac{1}{9}$ D $9\frac{1}{5}$

16. Which is correct?

F $\frac{2}{3} > \frac{3}{4}$ H $\frac{5}{7} < \frac{7}{8}$

G $\frac{4}{5} = \frac{8}{15}$ J $\frac{11}{20} > \frac{3}{5}$

17. Which shows the decimal for the picture?

A 0.48   C 0.40

B 0.52   D 0.50

18. Which shows $\frac{7}{9}$ as a decimal?

F 0.777   H $0.\overline{07}$

G $0.\overline{70}$ J $0.\overline{7}$

Section A: Factors and Multiples

Math Background

SKILLS 1 AND 2

Divisibility rules are helpful to determine the factors of large numbers. Every number has at least two factors, 1 and itself. Numbers that are odd will not be divisible by any even factors. Any number greater than 1 whose only factors are 1 and itself is a prime number. A number that has factors other than 1 and itself is composite. The number 1 is neither prime nor composite. Be sure to check a sufficient number of possible factors before determining that a number is prime.

SKILL 3

The prime factorization of a number is the product of all prime factors of that number. Composite numbers are not included in any prime factorization. When prime factoring, begin with a factor that seems obvious such as 2, 5, or 10.

SKILLS 4 AND 5

The number that is used as a factor is the *base*. The number that tells how many times the base is used as a factor is the *exponent*. In 3^5, 3 is the base and 5 is the exponent. 3^5 means $3 \times 3 \times 3 \times 3 \times 3$.

A common mistake is to multiply the base and the exponent. 3^5 does not mean 3×5. Exponents can be used to write a prime factorization in a more compact form.

$48 = 2 \times 2 \times 2 \times 2 \times 3 = 2^4 \times 3$.

SKILL 6

The greatest common factor (GCF) of a set of numbers is the largest number that is a factor of each number in the set. A common mistake is to find a factor that is common, but not the *greatest* of those that are common.

SKILL 7

The least common multiple (LCM) of a set of numbers is the smallest number that is a multiple of each number in the set. A common mistake is to simply find the product of the numbers in the set. Although 96 is a multiple of both 8 and 12, it is not the *least* common multiple.

SKILL 8

A useful strategy when solving problems is to draw a diagram to picture the information in the problem. Students should label diagrams appropriately.

Transparencies

Transparency 1 can be used to help students understand how a factor tree is used.

Use with Skill 3.

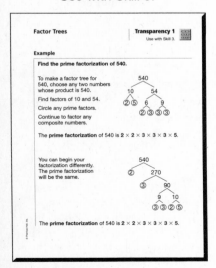

Transparency 2 can be used to demonstrate the difference between common factors and the greatest common factor (GCF).

Use with Skill 6.

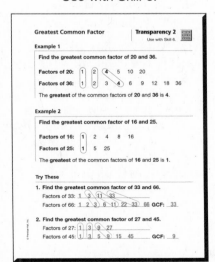

Transparency 3 can be used to demonstrate the difference between common multiples and the least common multiple (LCM).

Use with Skill 7.

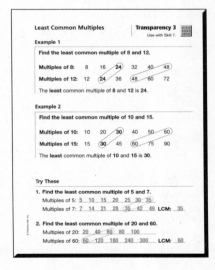

SKILL 1:
Factors and Divisibility

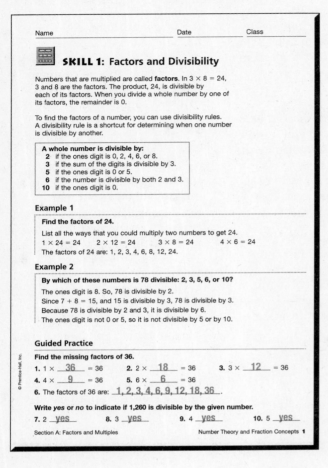

Name _____ Date _____ Class _____

SKILL 1: Factors and Divisibility

Numbers that are multiplied are called **factors**. In $3 \times 8 = 24$, 3 and 8 are the factors. The product, 24, is divisible by each of its factors. When you divide a whole number by one of its factors, the remainder is 0.

To find the factors of a number, you can use divisibility rules. A divisibility rule is a shortcut for determining when one number is divisible by another.

> **A whole number is divisible by:**
> **2** if the ones digit is 0, 2, 4, 6, or 8.
> **3** if the sum of the digits is divisible by 3.
> **5** if the ones digit is 0 or 5.
> **6** if the number is divisible by both 2 and 3.
> **10** if the ones digit is 0.

Example 1

Find the factors of 24.

List all the ways that you could multiply two numbers to get 24.
$1 \times 24 = 24$ $2 \times 12 = 24$ $3 \times 8 = 24$ $4 \times 6 = 24$
The factors of 24 are: 1, 2, 3, 4, 6, 8, 12, 24.

Example 2

By which of these numbers is 78 divisible: 2, 3, 5, 6, or 10?

The ones digit is 8. So, 78 is divisible by 2.
Since $7 + 8 = 15$, and 15 is divisible by 3, 78 is divisible by 3.
Because 78 is divisible by 2 and 3, it is divisible by 6.
The ones digit is not 0 or 5, so it is not divisible by 5 or by 10.

Guided Practice

Find the missing factors of 36.

1. $1 \times$ __36__ $= 36$ 2. $2 \times$ __18__ $= 36$ 3. $3 \times$ __12__ $= 36$
4. $4 \times$ __9__ $= 36$ 5. $6 \times$ __6__ $= 36$
6. The factors of 36 are: __1, 2, 3, 4, 6, 9, 12, 18, 36__.

Write yes or no to indicate if 1,260 is divisible by the given number.

7. 2 __yes__   8. 3 __yes__   9. 4 __yes__   10. 5 __yes__

Section A: Factors and Multiples   Number Theory and Fraction Concepts **1**

Name _____ Date _____ Class _____

SKILL 1: Practice

Answer each question.

1. Which of the following are factors of 16: 1, 2, 3, 4, 5, 6, 7, 8? __1, 2, 4, 8__
2. Which of the following are factors of 20: 1, 2, 3, 4, 5, 6, 7, 8? __1, 2, 4, 5__
3. List all factors of 28. __1, 2, 4, 7, 14, 28__
4. List all factors of 48. __1, 2, 3, 4, 6, 8, 12, 16, 24, 48__
5. List all factors of 100. __1, 2, 4, 5, 10, 20, 25, 50, 100__

Complete the table. Write yes or no.

	Divisible by:				
	2	3	5	6	10
6. 28	yes	no	no	no	no
7. 40	yes	no	yes	no	yes
8. 72	yes	yes	no	yes	no
9. 144	yes	yes	no	yes	no
10. 225	no	yes	yes	no	no
11. 360	yes	yes	yes	yes	yes
12. 504	yes	yes	no	yes	no
13. 600	yes	yes	yes	yes	yes

14. There are 365 days in a non-leap year.
By which of these numbers is 365 divisible: 2, 3, 5, 6, 10? __5__

15. Which is not a factor of 54?   *Skill 1*
   A 6   C 9
   (B) 7   D 27

16. Which is not divisible by 6?   *Skill 1*
   F 42   (H) 123
   G 132   J 522

2 Number Theory and Fraction Concepts   Section A: Factors and Multiples

---

Objective

Use divisibility rules to find the factors of a given number.

AS STUDENTS WORK...

Guided Practice Emphasize that when one number is divided by another so that the remainder is 0, the second number is a factor of the first.

Guided Practice 1–6 Students are first given one factor and asked to find the other. For Guided Practice 6, they gather all factors used in Guided Practice 1–5.

Guided Practice 7–10 Refer students to the divisibility rules near the top of the page.

Practice 3–5 Students are to list *all* factors of the given number. Remind them not to forget 1 and the number itself. For Practice 5, students should list the factor 10 only once.

Practice 6–14 Again refer students to the divisibility rules on page 1.

Error Alert Students often try to apply the divisibility test for 3 to other numbers. For example, they assume that because the sum of the digits of 574 is a number divisible by 4 (16), that 574 is divisible by 4. Point out that adding the digits can only be used as a divisibility test for 3 and 9.

TEST PREP

Error Analysis/Skills Trace

Answer	Work needed	Skill
15 A, C, or D	Understanding the meaning of factor	N1
16 F, G, or J	Understanding the meaning of divisible	N1

Skills Intervention Kit units that are referenced above:

N = Number Theory and Fraction Concepts

The above table may be used to analyze student errors. The table shows which skills in the kit address work that may be needed.

SKILL 2:
Primes and Composites

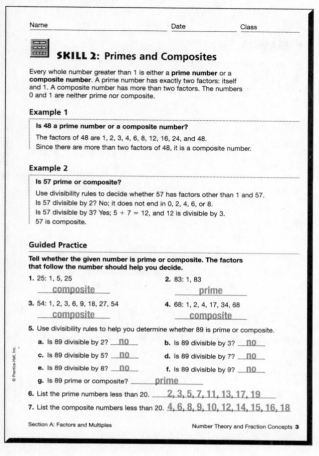

Name _____ Date _____ Class _____

SKILL 2: Primes and Composites

Every whole number greater than 1 is either a **prime number** or a **composite number**. A prime number has exactly two factors: itself and 1. A composite number has more than two factors. The numbers 0 and 1 are neither prime nor composite.

Example 1

Is 48 a prime number or a composite number?

The factors of 48 are 1, 2, 3, 4, 6, 8, 12, 16, 24, and 48.
Since there are more than two factors of 48, it is a composite number.

Example 2

Is 57 prime or composite?

Use divisibility rules to decide whether 57 has factors other than 1 and 57.
Is 57 divisible by 2? No; it does not end in 0, 2, 4, 6, or 8.
Is 57 divisible by 3? Yes; 5 + 7 = 12, and 12 is divisible by 3.
57 is composite.

Guided Practice

Tell whether the given number is prime or composite. The factors that follow the number should help you decide.

1. 25: 1, 5, 25   2. 83: 1, 83
   __composite__   __prime__

3. 54: 1, 2, 3, 6, 9, 18, 27, 54   4. 68: 1, 2, 4, 17, 34, 68
   __composite__   __composite__

5. Use divisibility rules to help you determine whether 89 is prime or composite.

   a. Is 89 divisible by 2? __no__   b. Is 89 divisible by 3? __no__
   c. Is 89 divisible by 5? __no__   d. Is 89 divisible by 7? __no__
   e. Is 89 divisible by 8? __no__   f. Is 89 divisible by 9? __no__
   g. Is 89 prime or composite? __prime__

6. List the prime numbers less than 20. __2, 3, 5, 7, 11, 13, 17, 19__
7. List the composite numbers less than 20. __4, 6, 8, 9, 10, 12, 14, 15, 16, 18__

Section A: Factors and Multiples   Number Theory and Fraction Concepts **3**

Name _____ Date _____ Class _____

SKILL 2: Practice

Tell whether the given number is prime or composite. The factors that follow the number should help you decide.

1. 92: 1, 2, 4, 23, 46, 92   2. 121: 1, 11, 121   3. 73: 1, 73
   __composite__   __composite__   __prime__

4. 129: 1, 3, 43, 129   5. 52: 1, 2, 4, 13, 26, 52   6. 55: 1, 5, 11, 55
   __composite__   __composite__   __composite__

7. 29: 1, 29   8. 57: 1, 3, 19, 57   9. 63: 1, 3, 7, 9, 21, 63
   __prime__   __composite__   __composite__

Tell whether each number is prime or composite.

10. 93 __composite__   11. 145 __composite__

12. 79 __prime__   13. 280 __composite__

14. 69 __composite__   15. 59 __prime__

16. 102 __composite__   17. 43 __prime__

18. 86 __composite__   19. 123 __composite__

Solve.

20. The Brentwood Orchestra has 161 members. Is the number of members prime or composite? __composite__

21. The local Hiking Trails and Open Spaces organization has 49 members. If a committee of the organization has a prime number of members, and that number is a factor of 49, then how many members are on the committee? __7__

22. Which of the following is a prime number?   *Skill 2*
    A 91   C 49
    B 75   (D) 97

23. Which of the following is not divisible by 4?   *Skill 1*
    F 1,264   H 1,332
    (G) 414   J 748

4 Number Theory and Fraction Concepts   Section A: Factors and Multiples

---

Objective
Determine whether numbers are prime or composite.

AS STUDENTS WORK...

Guided Practice Point out that every number greater than 1 has at least two factors, 1 and itself. The numbers greater than 1 that have only those factors are prime. If a number has more than those two factors, it is composite.

Guided Practice 5 Review the divisibility rules from Skill 1.

Guided Practice 6–7 Remind students that the number 1 is neither prime nor composite and therefore should not be included in either list.

Point out that if a number is odd, it will not have any even factors.

Practice 10–21 Students may have difficulty knowing when to stop testing for possible factors. In Practice 12, since 79 is between 64 (8 × 8) and 81 (9 × 9), students can stop testing numbers after they have tried all possible factors less than 9.

Error Alert Students occasionally assume larger numbers that are odd are prime if they cannot immediately think of any factors for the number. Emphasize that students should use the divisibility rules.

TEST PREP

Error Analysis/Skills Trace

Answer	Work needed	Skill
22 A, B, or C	Understanding the meaning of prime	N2
23 F, H, or J	Use of divisibility rules	N1

N = Number Theory and Fraction Concepts

SKILL 3:
Prime Factorization

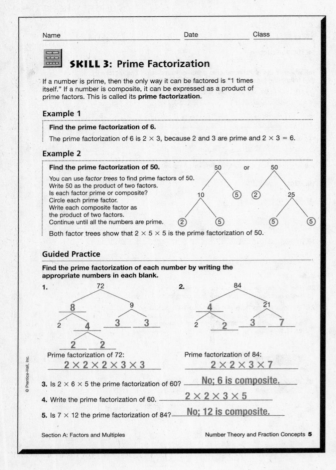

SKILL 3: Prime Factorization

If a number is prime, then the only way it can be factored is "1 times itself." If a number is composite, it can be expressed as a product of prime factors. This is called its **prime factorization**.

Example 1

Find the prime factorization of 6.

The prime factorization of 6 is 2 × 3, because 2 and 3 are prime and 2 × 3 = 6.

Example 2

Find the prime factorization of 50.

You can use *factor trees* to find prime factors of 50.
Write 50 as the product of two factors.
Is each factor prime or composite?
Circle each prime factor.
Write each composite factor as
the product of two factors.
Continue until all the numbers are prime.

Both factor trees show that 2 × 5 × 5 is the prime factorization of 50.

Guided Practice

Find the prime factorization of each number by writing the appropriate numbers in each blank.

1. 72 = 8 × 9 ; 8 = 2 × 4 ; 4 = 2 × 2 ; 9 = 3 × 3

Prime factorization of 72:
2 × 2 × 2 × 3 × 3

2. 84 = 4 × 21 ; 4 = 2 × 2 ; 21 = 3 × 7

Prime factorization of 84:
2 × 2 × 3 × 7

3. Is 2 × 6 × 5 the prime factorization of 60? No; 6 is composite.

4. Write the prime factorization of 60. 2 × 2 × 3 × 5

5. Is 7 × 12 the prime factorization of 84? No; 12 is composite.

Section A: Factors and Multiples — Number Theory and Fraction Concepts **5**

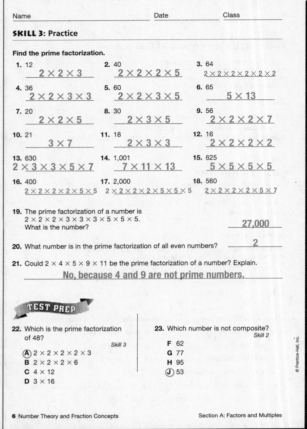

SKILL 3: Practice

Find the prime factorization.

1. 12 2 × 2 × 3
2. 40 2 × 2 × 2 × 5
3. 64 2 × 2 × 2 × 2 × 2 × 2
4. 36 2 × 2 × 3 × 3
5. 60 2 × 2 × 3 × 5
6. 65 5 × 13
7. 20 2 × 2 × 5
8. 30 2 × 3 × 5
9. 56 2 × 2 × 2 × 7
10. 21 3 × 7
11. 18 2 × 3 × 3
12. 16 2 × 2 × 2 × 2
13. 630 2 × 3 × 3 × 5 × 7
14. 1,001 7 × 11 × 13
15. 625 5 × 5 × 5 × 5
16. 400 2 × 2 × 2 × 2 × 5 × 5
17. 2,000 2 × 2 × 2 × 2 × 5 × 5 × 5
18. 560 2 × 2 × 2 × 2 × 5 × 7

19. The prime factorization of a number is
2 × 2 × 2 × 3 × 3 × 3 × 5 × 5 × 5.
What is the number?   27,000

20. What number is in the prime factorization of all even numbers?   2

21. Could 2 × 4 × 5 × 9 × 11 be the prime factorization of a number? Explain.
No, because 4 and 9 are not prime numbers.

TEST PREP

22. Which is the prime factorization of 48?   *Skill 3*
Ⓐ 2 × 2 × 2 × 2 × 3
B 2 × 2 × 2 × 6
C 4 × 12
D 3 × 16

23. Which number is not composite?   *Skill 2*
F 62
G 77
H 95
Ⓙ 53

6 Number Theory and Fraction Concepts — Section A: Factors and Multiples

---

Objective

Find the prime factorization of composite numbers.

 Transparency 1
can be useful with a group of students.

AS STUDENTS WORK...

Guided Practice 1 and 2
Where one factor is provided, students are to provide the missing factor to give the product just above.

Guided Practice 3–5 Students should recognize that a set of factors cannot be a prime factorization unless all of the factors are prime. Use the factorization given in Guided Practice 3 to help students find the *prime* factorization asked for in Guided Practice 4.

Practice 1–18 Remind students that they may not include any composite numbers in the prime factorizations.

Practice 19 Students may find it easier to multiply all the factors if they pair up the 2s and the 5s to make three factors of 10. They would thus have 10 × 10 × 10 × 3 × 3 × 3.

Practice 20 A follow-up would be to discuss that all even numbers greater than 2 are composite.

Error Alert Watch for students who include composite numbers in their prime factorizations.

TEST PREP

Error Analysis/Skills Trace

Answer	Work needed	Skill
22 B, C, or D	Finding prime factorization	N3
23 F, G, or H	Understanding the meaning of composite	N2

N = Number Theory and Fraction Concepts

SKILL 4:
Exponents

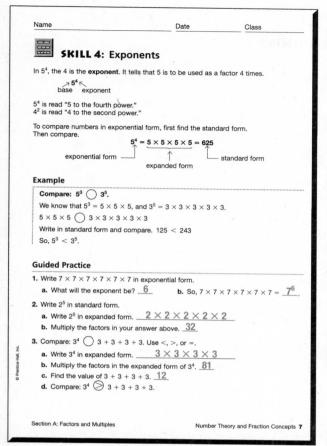

Name _____ Date _____ Class _____

SKILL 4: Exponents

In 5^4, the 4 is the **exponent**. It tells that 5 is to be used as a factor 4 times.

$$5^4$$
base   exponent

5^4 is read "5 to the fourth power."
4^2 is read "4 to the second power."

To compare numbers in exponential form, first find the standard form. Then compare.

$$5^4 = 5 \times 5 \times 5 \times 5 = 625$$

exponential form — expanded form — standard form

Example

Compare: 5^3 ◯ 3^5.

We know that $5^3 = 5 \times 5 \times 5$, and $3^5 = 3 \times 3 \times 3 \times 3 \times 3$.

$5 \times 5 \times 5$ ◯ $3 \times 3 \times 3 \times 3 \times 3$

Write in standard form and compare. 125 < 243

So, $5^3 < 3^5$.

Guided Practice

1. Write $7 \times 7 \times 7 \times 7 \times 7 \times 7$ in exponential form.
   a. What will the exponent be? __6__
   b. So, $7 \times 7 \times 7 \times 7 \times 7 \times 7 = $ __7^6__ .

2. Write 2^5 in standard form.
   a. Write 2^5 in expanded form. __$2 \times 2 \times 2 \times 2 \times 2$__
   b. Multiply the factors in your answer above. __32__

3. Compare: 3^4 ◯ $3 + 3 + 3 + 3$. Use <, >, or =.
   a. Write 3^4 in expanded form. __$3 \times 3 \times 3 \times 3$__
   b. Multiply the factors in the expanded form of 3^4. __81__
   c. Find the value of $3 + 3 + 3 + 3$. __12__
   d. Compare: 3^4 ⊖ $3 + 3 + 3 + 3$.

Section A: Factors and Multiples

Number Theory and Fraction Concepts **7**

Name _____ Date _____ Class _____

SKILL 4: Practice

Write in exponential form.

1. $3 \times 3 \times 3 \times 3 \times 3 \times 3$ __3^6__
2. 53×53 __53^2__
3. $2 \times 2 \times 2 \times 2 \times 2 \times 2 \times 2$ __2^7__
4. $13 \times 13 \times 13$ __13^3__
5. $8 \times 8 \times 8 \times 8$ __8^4 or 2^{12}__
6. 17×17 __17^2__

Write in expanded form.

7. 10^4 __$10 \times 10 \times 10 \times 10$__
8. 6^5 __$6 \times 6 \times 6 \times 6 \times 6$__
9. 3^2 __3×3__
10. 7^3 __$7 \times 7 \times 7$__
11. 12^4 __$12 \times 12 \times 12 \times 12$__
12. 5^6 __$5 \times 5 \times 5 \times 5 \times 5 \times 5$__

Write in standard form.

13. 5^4 __625__
14. 2^6 __64__
15. 10^7 __10,000,000__
16. 11^2 __121__
17. 12^2 __144__
18. 6^3 __216__

Compare using <, >, or =.

19. 7^3 ⊖ $7 + 7 + 7$
20. 3^4 ⊖ 4^3
21. 4×10 ⊖ 10^4

Solve.

22. The highest point in Kentucky is Black Mountain. Its height is about 2^{12} feet. About how high is Black Mountain? __4,096 feet__

23. Celeste had 3¢ on Day 1. She had three times that much on Day 2. On Day 3 she had three times as much as she had on Day 2. If she continues this pattern, on what day will she have 2,187¢? __Day 7__

 **TEST PREP**

24. Which is 4^3 in standard form?
    Skill 4
    A 12   C 64
    B 7   D 4

25. Which shows a prime factorization?
    Skill 3
    F $2 \times 2 \times 3 \times 5$ H $3 \times 4 \times 5$
    G $2 \times 3 \times 5 \times 6$ J 9×12

8 Number Theory and Fraction Concepts

Section A: Factors and Multiples

Objective

Use exponents.

AS STUDENTS WORK...

Guided Practice It is important that students realize that the exponent is the number of times the base is used as a factor. Point out the difference between expanded form and standard form.

Guided Practice 3 Remind students of the meaning of the < and > signs. After doing this exercise, students may want to discuss the difference in the results found by adding four 3s and by multiplying four 3s.

Practice 1–12 Remind students that the base is the number used as a factor; the exponent is the number of factors that are multiplied.

Practice 13–18 Most students will need to write the number in expanded form first.

Practice 23 Help students to see the pattern. On Day 1, Celeste had 3¢; on Day 2 she had 9¢; on Day 3 she had 27¢; and so on.

Error Alert Watch for students who multiply the base and the exponent.

TEST PREP

Error Analysis/Skills Trace

Answer	Work needed	Skill
24 A, B, or D	Writing an expression with an exponent in standard form	N4
25 G, H, or J	Recognizing prime factored form	N3

N = Number Theory and Fraction Concepts

SKILL 5:
Prime Factorization with Exponents

Name   Date   Class

SKILL 5: Prime Factorization with Exponents

You can use exponents to express prime factorization in a compact form. For example, 125 is equal to $5 \times 5 \times 5$ or 5^3.

To write the prime factorization of 360 in exponential form, first write the factors in expanded form.

$$360 = 2 \times 2 \times 2 \times 3 \times 3 \times 5$$

Use exponents to show the number of identical factors.

two factors of $3 = 3^2$

$2 \times 2 \times 2 \times \overline{3 \times 3} \times 5 = 2^3 \times 3^2 \times 5$

three factors of $2 = 2^3$

$5 = 5^1$, but you need not write the exponent.

So, the exponential form of the prime factorization of 360 is $2^3 \times 3^2 \times 5$.

Example

Write the prime factorization $3^3 \times 5^2$ in standard form.

First write in expanded form. $3^3 \times 5^2 = \underline{3 \times 3 \times 3} \times \underline{5 \times 5} = 675$
Then multiply.   27   ×   25
The standard form of the number $3^3 \times 5^2$ is 675.

Guided Practice

1. Write $2 \times 2 \times 3 \times 3 \times 3 \times 5 \times 5$ using exponents.

$2 \times 2 \times 3 \times 3 \times 3 \times 5 \times 5 = 2^{\boxed{2}} \times 3^{\boxed{3}} \times 5^{\boxed{2}}$

2. Write the prime factorization $2^3 \times 7^2$ in standard form.

   a. Write 2^3 in expanded form. $2 \times 2 \times 2$

   b. Multiply the factors in part a.   8

   c. Write 7^2 in expanded form. 7×7

   d. Multiply the factors in part c.   49

   e. Multiply the numbers you found in parts b and d.   392

   f. So, $2^3 \times 7^2 = 2 \times \underline{2} \times \underline{2} \times 7 \times \underline{7} = 8 \times \underline{49} = \underline{392}$.

Section A: Factors and Multiples   Number Theory and Fraction Concepts **9**

Name   Date   Class

SKILL 5: Practice

Write the prime factorization for each number in expanded form as a product of individual factors. Then write each prime factorization using exponents.

1. 144
$2 \times 2 \times 2 \times 2 \times 3 \times 3$
$2^4 \times 3^2$

2. 90
$2 \times 3 \times 3 \times 5$
$2 \times 3^2 \times 5$

3. 1,925
$5 \times 5 \times 7 \times 11$
$5^2 \times 7 \times 11$

4. 480
$2 \times 2 \times 2 \times 2 \times 2 \times 3 \times 5$
$2^5 \times 3 \times 5$

5. 405
$3 \times 3 \times 3 \times 3 \times 5$
$3^4 \times 5$

6. 444
$2 \times 2 \times 3 \times 37$
$2^2 \times 3 \times 37$

7. 128
$2 \times 2 \times 2 \times 2 \times 2 \times 2 \times 2$
2^7

8. 225
$3 \times 3 \times 5 \times 5$
$3^2 \times 5^2$

9. 2,600
$2 \times 2 \times 2 \times 5 \times 5 \times 13$
$2^3 \times 5^2 \times 13$

Write each prime factorization in expanded form. Then write the number in standard form.

10. $2^3 \times 3 \times 5^3$
$2 \times 2 \times 2 \times 3 \times 5 \times 5 \times 5$
3,000

11. $2^2 \times 3^3 \times 7^2 \times 11$
$2 \times 2 \times 3 \times 3 \times 3 \times 7 \times 7 \times 11$
58,212

12. Luis used exponents to write this prime factorization for a number: $2^3 \times 3^3 \times 5^3$
What is the standard form for this number?   27,000

13. Which is the prime factorization for 720 using exponents?   *Skill 5*
   A $2 \times 2 \times 2 \times 2 \times 3 \times 3 \times 5$
   B $2^4 \times 3^2 \times 5$
   C $2^3 \times 3^2 \times 5$
   D $2 + 2 + 2 + 2 + 3 + 3 + 5$

14. Which is 7^3 in standard form?   *Skill 4*
   F 21
   G 37
   H 73
   J 343

10 Number Theory and Fraction Concepts   Section A: Factors and Multiples

---

Objective

Write prime factorizations using exponents.

AS STUDENTS WORK...

Guided Practice 1 Students should group all the like prime factors together to determine each exponent.

Guided Practice 2 Point out that it is often helpful to multiply all the like factors together, then multiply those products.

Practice Students should group like factors together for these exercises.

Practice 1–9 Emphasize first writing the prime factorization as a product of all the necessary factors, then writing

that expression using exponents.

Practice 12 Students may find it easier to multiply 8 (2^3) and 125 (5^3) first, then multiply that product by 27.

Error Alert Watch for students who miss one of the factors of 2 in Practice 4 and 7. Also watch for students who multiply base and exponent in Practice 10–12.

TEST PREP

Error Analysis/Skills Trace

Answer	Work needed	Skill
13 A	Use of exponents	N5
13 C or D	Recognizing prime factored form	N3
14 F, G, or H	Writing expressions with exponents in standard form	N4

N = Number Theory and Fraction Concepts

SKILL 6:
Greatest Common Factor

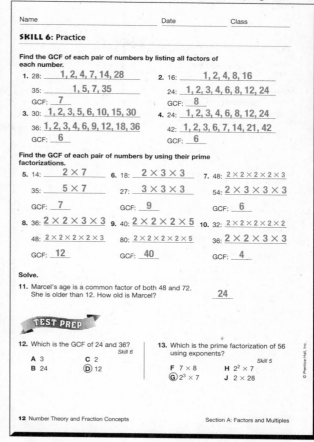

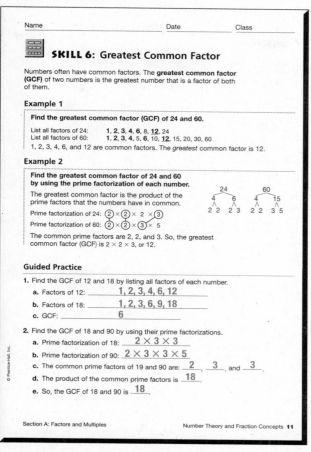

Name _____ Date _____ Class _____

SKILL 6: Greatest Common Factor

Numbers often have common factors. The **greatest common factor (GCF)** of two numbers is the greatest number that is a factor of both of them.

Example 1

Find the greatest common factor (GCF) of 24 and 60.

List all factors of 24: **1, 2, 3, 4,** 6, 8, **12,** 24
List all factors of 60: **1, 2, 3, 4,** 5, **6,** 10, **12,** 15, 20, 30, 60
1, 2, 3, 4, 6, and 12 are common factors. The *greatest* common factor is 12.

Example 2

Find the greatest common factor of 24 and 60 by using the prime factorization of each number.

The greatest common factor is the product of the prime factors that the numbers have in common.
Prime factorization of 24: $2 \times 2 \times 2 \times 3$
Prime factorization of 60: $2 \times 2 \times 3 \times 5$
The common prime factors are 2, 2, and 3. So, the greatest common factor (GCF) is $2 \times 2 \times 3$, or 12.

Guided Practice

1. Find the GCF of 12 and 18 by listing all factors of each number.
   a. Factors of 12: __1, 2, 3, 4, 6, 12__
   b. Factors of 18: __1, 2, 3, 6, 9, 18__
   c. GCF: __6__

2. Find the GCF of 18 and 90 by using their prime factorizations.
   a. Prime factorization of 18: __$2 \times 3 \times 3$__
   b. Prime factorization of 90: __$2 \times 3 \times 3 \times 5$__
   c. The common prime factors of 19 and 90 are: __2__, __3__, and __3__.
   d. The product of the common prime factors is __18__.
   e. So, the GCF of 18 and 90 is __18__.

Section A: Factors and Multiples — Number Theory and Fraction Concepts **11**

Name _____ Date _____ Class _____

SKILL 6: Practice

Find the GCF of each pair of numbers by listing all factors of each number.

1. 28: __1, 2, 4, 7, 14, 28__
   35: __1, 5, 7, 35__
   GCF: __7__

2. 16: __1, 2, 4, 8, 16__
   24: __1, 2, 3, 4, 6, 8, 12, 24__
   GCF: __8__

3. 30: __1, 2, 3, 5, 6, 10, 15, 30__
   36: __1, 2, 3, 4, 6, 9, 12, 18, 36__
   GCF: __6__

4. 24: __1, 2, 3, 4, 6, 8, 12, 24__
   42: __1, 2, 3, 6, 7, 14, 21, 42__
   GCF: __6__

Find the GCF of each pair of numbers by using their prime factorizations.

5. 14: __2×7__
   35: __5×7__
   GCF: __7__

6. 18: __$2 \times 3 \times 3$__
   27: __$3 \times 3 \times 3$__
   GCF: __9__

7. 48: __$2 \times 2 \times 2 \times 2 \times 3$__
   54: __$2 \times 3 \times 3 \times 3$__
   GCF: __6__

8. 36: __$2 \times 2 \times 3 \times 3$__
   48: __$2 \times 2 \times 2 \times 2 \times 3$__
   GCF: __12__

9. 40: __$2 \times 2 \times 2 \times 5$__
   80: __$2 \times 2 \times 2 \times 2 \times 5$__
   GCF: __40__

10. 32: __$2 \times 2 \times 2 \times 2 \times 2$__
    36: __$2 \times 2 \times 3 \times 3$__
    GCF: __4__

Solve.

11. Marcel's age is a common factor of both 48 and 72. She is older than 12. How old is Marcel? __24__

12. Which is the GCF of 24 and 36? *Skill 6*
    A 3 C 2
    B 24 (D) 12

13. Which is the prime factorization of 56 using exponents? *Skill 5*
    F 7×8 H $2^2 \times 7$
    (G) $2^3 \times 7$ J 2×28

12 Number Theory and Fraction Concepts — Section A: Factors and Multiples

---

Objective

Find the greatest common factor (GCF) of two numbers.

Transparency 2 can be useful with a group of students.

AS STUDENTS WORK...

Guided Practice Students may find it easier to find all factors of a number if they look for pairs of factors.

Point out that the number 1 is used when listing all factors of a number, but it is not used in the prime factorization.

Guided Practice 1 Although 2, 3, and 6 are common factors of both 12 and 18, 6 is the *greatest* factor. Thus, the GCF of 12 and 18 is 6.

Practice 1–4 Students may want to draw lines connecting pairs of common factors to more easily see the greatest common factor.

Practice 5–10 Students may want to indicate pairs of common prime factors, by using lines or by ringing the factors. Only those factors common to both numbers may be used.

TEST PREP

Error Analysis/Skills Trace

Answer	Work needed	Skill
12 A, B, or C	Finding the GCF	N6
13 F or J	Finding prime factorization	N3
13 H	Using exponents	N5

N = Number Theory and Fraction Concepts

SKILL 7:
Least Common Multiple

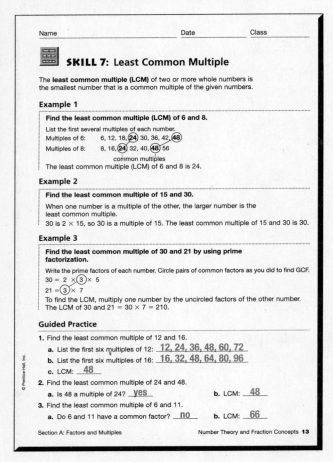

Name _____ Date _____ Class _____

SKILL 7: Least Common Multiple

The **least common multiple (LCM)** of two or more whole numbers is the smallest number that is a common multiple of the given numbers.

Example 1

Find the least common multiple (LCM) of 6 and 8.

List the first several multiples of each number.
Multiples of 6: 6, 12, 18, ㉔ 30, 36, 42, ㊽
Multiples of 8: 8, 16, ㉔ 32, 40, ㊽ 56
          common multiples
The least common multiple (LCM) of 6 and 8 is 24.

Example 2

Find the least common multiple of 15 and 30.

When one number is a multiple of the other, the larger number is the least common multiple.
30 is 2 × 15, so 30 is a multiple of 15. The least common multiple of 15 and 30 is 30.

Example 3

Find the least common multiple of 30 and 21 by using prime factorization.

Write the prime factors of each number. Circle pairs of common factors as you did to find GCF.
30 = 2 × ③ × 5
21 = ③ × 7
To find the LCM, multiply one number by the uncircled factors of the other number.
The LCM of 30 and 21 = 30 × 7 = 210.

Guided Practice

1. Find the least common multiple of 12 and 16.
   a. List the first six multiples of 12: __12, 24, 36, 48, 60, 72__
   b. List the first six multiples of 16: __16, 32, 48, 64, 80, 96__
   c. LCM: __48__
2. Find the least common multiple of 24 and 48.
   a. Is 48 a multiple of 24? __yes__   b. LCM: __48__
3. Find the least common multiple of 6 and 11.
   a. Do 6 and 11 have a common factor? __no__   b. LCM: __66__

Section A: Factors and Multiples   Number Theory and Fraction Concepts **13**

Name _____ Date _____ Class _____

SKILL 7: Practice

Find the LCM of each pair of numbers by listing multiples of each number. Number of multiples given may vary.

1. 3: __3, 6, 9, 12, 15, 18__   2. 3: __3, 6, 9, 12, 15, 18__
   2: __2, 4, 6, 8, 10, 12__   4: __4, 8, 12, 16, 20, 24__
   LCM: __6__   LCM: __12__
3. 5: __5, 10, 15, 20, 25, 30__   4. 2: __2, 4, 6, 8, 10, 12__
   4: __4, 8, 12, 16, 20, 24__   8: __8, 16, 24, 32, 40, 48__
   LCM: __20__   LCM: __8__

Find the LCM of each pair.

5. 6, 5 __30__   6. 3, 21 __21__   7. 9, 5 __45__
8. 17, 3 __51__   9. 6, 23 __138__   10. 21, 7 __21__
11. 6, 28 __84__   12. 14, 18 __126__   13. 23, 2 __46__
14. 11, 33 __33__ 15. 6, 10 __30__   16. 36, 45 __180__
17. 31, 5 __155__ 18. 10, 14 __70__   19. 22, 4 __44__
20. 20, 30 __60__ 21. 29, 3 __87__   22. 16, 18 __144__
23. 12, 18 __36__ 24. 20, 25 __100__   25. 15, 40 __120__

Solve.

26. Hot dogs come 8 to a package. Buns come 6 to a package. What is the fewest number of packages of each you would have to buy so that you have exactly as many hot dogs as buns?

__3__ packages of hot dogs; __4__ packages of buns

27. Which is the LCM of 15 and 24?   28. Which is the GCF of 24 and 40?
                              Skill 7   *Skill 6*
   A 3   C 9   F 960   (H) 8
   (B) 120   D 360   G 120   J 4

14 Number Theory and Fraction Concepts   Section A: Factors and Multiples

---

Objective

Find the least common multiple (LCM) of two numbers.

Transparency 3 can be useful with a group of students.

AS STUDENTS WORK...

Guided Practice Point out that sometimes more than six multiples may be needed to find the LCM.

Point out that if there is more than one common multiple in the listings, students are looking for the *least*.

Practice Students will need to list enough multiples until there is a multiple that is common to both numbers.

Practice 26 Help students to realize that the LCM of 8 and 6 is 24, so they should divide 24 by 8 and by 6.

Error Alert Watch for students who just multiply the two numbers together in Practice 5–25. For students having difficulty, have them list multiples for each number and then choose the least of those.

TEST PREP

Error Analysis/Skills Trace

Answer	Work needed	Skill
27 A, C, or D	Finding the LCM	N7
28 F, G, or J	Finding the GCF	N6

N = Number Theory and Fraction Concepts

SKILL 8: PROBLEM SOLVING:
Draw a Diagram

Name _____ Date _____ Class _____

SKILL 8: PROBLEM SOLVING:
Draw a Diagram

Solving a problem can often be easier if you draw a diagram or picture to help you understand the problem.

Example

Marti has Sunday off, then works Monday through Saturday, so she has a day off once every 7 days. She needs to give her dog some medicine every 3 days. How often does she give her dog medicine on her day off?

Read Marti's days off occur every 7 days. Her dog needs medicine every 3 days.

Plan Draw a diagram of several weeks on a calendar. Label her days off with "Off." Label the days her dog needs medicine with "M."

Solve Start with a Sunday she is off and she gives medicine. Find the next day that this happens.

Sun.	Mon.	Tues.	Wed.	Thurs.	Fri.	Sat.
Off/M			M			M
Off		M			M	
Off	M			M		
Off/M						

Twenty-one days later, Marti has a day off and her dog needs medicine. She gives her dog medicine on her day off every 21 days.

Look Back Does your answer makes sense? The least common multiple of 7 and 3 is 21. It makes sense that an event occurring every 7 days and another event occurring every 3 days will occur together on the LCM of 7 and 3.

Guided Practice

Ari is buying buns and hamburgers for a picnic. Buns come 8 to a package. Hamburgers come 10 to a package. Ari would like to buy exactly as many hamburgers as buns.

1. Fill in the diagram with the number of items per package to illustrate the fewest number of packages of each item Ari should buy.

Buns
[8] [8] [8] [8] [8]
40 buns

Hamburgers
[10] [10] [10] [10]
40 hamburgers

2. How many buns and hamburgers will he buy? _40 buns; 40 hamburgers_

3. How many packages of each will this be?
_5_ packages of buns; _4_ packages of hamburgers

Name _____ Date _____ Class _____

SKILL 8: Practice

Solve each problem.

1. The bookstore sells packages of 15 pens each and 12 pencils each. They want the same number of pens and pencils in their next order. Find the smallest number of packages of each they can buy.

   4 packages of pens; 5 packages of pencils

2. Ms. Ling's chemistry class uses 10-gram weights and 25-gram weights on a balance scale. What is the smallest number of each needed to balance the scale?

   five 10-gram; two 25-gram

3. Freida wants to use the same number of black beads and white beads for a project. Black beads come in bags of 20. White beads come in bags of 15. What is the least number of bags of each color she can use?

   3 black; 4 white

4. All Sport Outdoor Store sells fruit energy bars in 6-bar packages. They also sell nut energy bars in 4-bar packages. If the store wants to order the same number of bars of both kinds, what is the least number of packages of each they can buy?

   two 6-bar; three 4-bar

5. The traffic signal at 4th and Main turns green every 6 minutes. The signal at 5th and Broadway turns green every 4 minutes. If both turned green at 12:15 P.M., when are the next three times that both will turn green at the same time?

   _12:27 P.M., 12:39 P.M., 12:51 P.M._

TEST PREP

6. Boxes that are 10 inches tall are stacked next to boxes that are 12 inches tall. Find the least number of each size box that could be stacked next to each other so that the stacks are the same height.
   Skill 7

   A two 10-in. and two 12-in.
   B twelve 10-in. and ten 12-in.
   (C) six 10-in. and five 12-in.
   D five 10-in. and six 12-in.

7. Find the GCF of 14 and 24.
   Skill 6

   F 168
   G 3
   (H) 2
   J 38

Objective

Draw a diagram to solve problems.

AS STUDENTS WORK...

Guided Practice It may help some students to keep a total of how many buns and how many hamburgers have been purchased.

Packages	Buns	Hamburgers
1	8	10
2	16	20
3	24	30
4	32	**40**
5	**40**	

When the same number of buns and hamburgers is found in the table, then read across to find the number of packages of each.

Practice Emphasize students' drawing a diagram for each problem. They may also want to keep a total of the number of each item that has been used.

Practice 1 For students having difficulty, have them label their diagram to show how many of each item they would be buying with various numbers of packages.

Packages	Pens	Pencils
1	15	12
2	30	24
3	45	36
4	**60**	48
5	75	**60**

Error Alert Watch for students who just multiply the number of items per package for each item together. Stress that the problems ask for the *least* number of each that can be used.

TEST PREP

Error Analysis/Skills Trace

Answer	Work needed	Skill
6 A, B, or D	Finding the appropriate number of each item using a diagram	N8
7 F, G, or J	Finding the GCF	N6

N = Number Theory and Fraction Concepts

Test Prep and Mixed Review for Section A

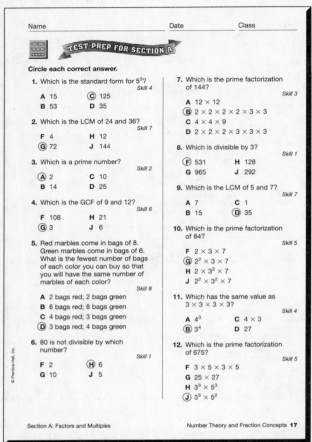

TEST PREP FOR SECTION A

Name _____ Date _____ Class _____

Circle each correct answer.

1. Which is the standard form for 5^3?
   Skill 4
   - A 15
   - Ⓒ 125
   - B 53
   - D 35

2. Which is the LCM of 24 and 36?
   Skill 7
   - F 4
   - H 12
   - Ⓖ 72
   - J 144

3. Which is a prime number?
   Skill 2
   - Ⓐ 2
   - C 10
   - B 14
   - D 25

4. Which is the GCF of 9 and 12?
   Skill 6
   - F 108
   - H 21
   - Ⓖ 3
   - J 6

5. Red marbles come in bags of 8. Green marbles come in bags of 6. What is the fewest number of bags of each color you can buy so that you will have the same number of marbles of each color?
   Skill 8
   - A 2 bags red; 2 bags green
   - B 6 bags red; 8 bags green
   - C 4 bags red; 3 bags green
   - Ⓓ 3 bags red; 4 bags green

6. 80 is not divisible by which number?
   Skill 1
   - F 2
   - Ⓗ 6
   - G 10
   - J 5

7. Which is the prime factorization of 144?
   Skill 3
   - A 12 × 12
   - Ⓑ 2 × 2 × 2 × 2 × 3 × 3
   - C 4 × 4 × 9
   - D 2 × 2 × 2 × 3 × 3 × 3

8. Which is divisible by 3?
   Skill 1
   - Ⓕ 531
   - H 128
   - G 965
   - J 292

9. Which is the LCM of 5 and 7?
   Skill 7
   - A 7
   - C 1
   - B 15
   - Ⓓ 35

10. Which is the prime factorization of 84?
    Skill 5
    - F 2 × 3 × 7
    - Ⓖ $2^2 × 3 × 7$
    - H $2 × 3^2 × 7$
    - J $2^2 × 3^2 × 7$

11. Which has the same value as 3 × 3 × 3 × 3?
    Skill 4
    - A 4^3
    - C 4 × 3
    - Ⓑ 3^4
    - D 27

12. Which is the prime factorization of 675?
    Skill 5
    - F 3 × 5 × 3 × 5
    - G 25 × 27
    - H $3^3 × 5^3$
    - Ⓙ $3^3 × 5^2$

Section A: Factors and Multiples

Number Theory and Fraction Concepts **17**

Mixed Review for Section A

Name _____ Date _____ Class _____

State Match-Up

Write each clue number in the blank beside the correct state's name. To check, see if the answer to the math exercise matches the clue number.

1. Its name contains something to write with.

2. Its name contains 4 identical vowels.

3. It is surrounded by water.

4. Its name contains the name of another state.

5. It has the same name as the capital of the United States.

6. Its southern tip is near Cuba.

7. It is the home of Pikes Peak in the Rocky Mountains.

8. Its name is the name of a potato.

9. It has a city that has the same name as the state.

Idaho The standard form for 2^3	8
Pennsylvania The number that is neither prime nor composite	1
Florida The LCM of 2 and 3	6
Hawaii The prime factorization of 27 contains this number.	3
Mississippi 32 is this number to the fifth power.	2
Colorado The number that is the prime number between 5 and 11	7
Arkansas The GCF of 20 and 36	4
New York This number is the product of two factors of 3.	9
Washington Rulers come in 4-packs. Erasers come in 10-packs. To buy the same number of each, buy this number pack of rulers and 2 packs of erasers.	5

18 Number Theory and Fraction Concepts

Section A: Factors and Multiples

TEST PREP

Error Analysis/Skills Trace

Answer	Work needed	Skill
1 A, B, or D	Writing an expression with an exponent in standard form	N4
2 F, H, or J	Finding the LCM	N7
3 B, C, or D	Understanding the meaning of prime	N2
4 F, H, or J	Finding the GCF	N6
5 A, B, or C	Finding the appropriate number of each item using a diagram	N8
6 F, G, or J	Understanding divisibility	N1
7 A, C, or D	Finding prime factorization	N3
8 G, H, or J	Understanding divisibility	N1
9 A, B, or C	Finding the LCM	N7
10 F, H, or J	Finding prime factorization using exponents	N5
11 A, C, or D	Using exponents	N4
12 F, G, or H	Finding prime factorization using exponents	N5

N = Number Theory and Fraction Concepts

Mixed Review

Point out to students that they should work the problems in the right-hand column first, then match each result with that statement number in the left-hand column.

---

12 Number Theory and Fraction Concepts

Section A: Factors and Multiples

Section B: Introduction to Fractions

Math Background

SKILL 9

Students should be aware that a fraction can be used to indicate a part of a whole or a part of a set. This skill introduces students to the meaning of the numerator and the denominator of a fraction although those terms are not used until Skill 11. When talking about fractional parts, it is important that students realize that the parts must be of equal size.

SKILL 10

Estimating is a valuable tool for students to develop. This skill focuses on getting students to visualize what the following fractional parts of a whole look like: $\frac{1}{4}$, $\frac{1}{3}$, $\frac{1}{2}$, $\frac{2}{3}$, $\frac{3}{4}$, or 1 whole. The goal is to accurately assess *about* how much is shaded.

SKILL 11

Equivalent fractions are fractions with different numerators and different denominators that name the same amount. They are used when comparing two fractions that represent different fractional parts of a whole or of a set. They are also used when adding and subtracting fractions.

SKILL 12

Most often, students will be asked to give their answers to fraction computation problems in lowest terms or simplest form. This skill is also used when multiplying and dividing fractions. Students need a firm understanding of equivalent fractions to grasp the process of writing fractions in simplest form. Some students may have used the term "reducing" to indicate the process of writing fractions in simplest form.

SKILL 13

Writing fractions with a common denominator is necessary when adding and subtracting fractions with unlike denominators. The preferred denominator is the *least* common denominator as it makes the computation easier.

Transparencies

Transparency 4 can be used to help students understand how a fraction can be used to express part of a whole or part of a set.

Use with Skill 9.

Transparency 5 can be used to help students visualize a fraction of a whole.

Use with Skill 10.

Transparency 6 can be used to demonstrate that equivalent fractions name the same amount.

Use with Skills 11–13.

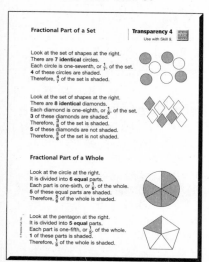

SKILL 9: Writing a Fraction as Part of a Set or Part of a Whole

Student pages 19–20

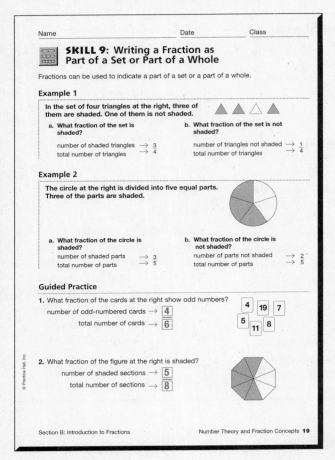

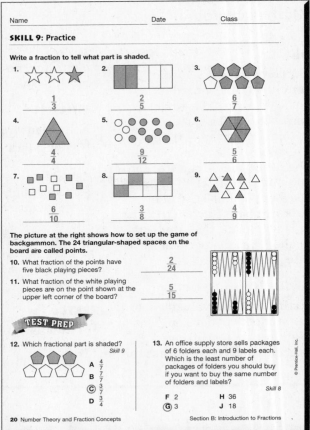

Objective

Write a fraction for a part of a whole or a part of a set.

Transparency 4 can be useful with a group of students.

AS STUDENTS WORK...

Guided Practice The emphasis in this skill is to get students to understand that the denominator indicates the total number of *equal* parts and the numerator indicates the number of parts being talked about. The terms numerator and denominator will be used beginning in Skill 11. Stress that the parts must be of equal size.

Guided Practice Have students first identify how many equal parts there are.

Practice 1–9 Remind students that they are to write a fraction for the *shaded* part.

Practice 10 and 11 Point out to students that in each exercise they will need to first determine the total number of parts: 24 total points for Practice 10 and 15 total pieces for Practice 11.

Error Alert Some students will try to write fractions that compare the number of shaded parts to the number of unshaded parts. They should understand that the *total* number of parts is the denominator of each fraction.

Error Analysis/Skills Trace

Answer	Work needed	Skill
12 A, B, or D	Writing a fraction for part of a set	N9
13 F, H, or J	Finding the appropriate number of each item using a diagram	N8

Skills Intervention Kit units that are referenced above:

N = Number Theory and Fraction Concepts

SKILL 10:
Estimating Fractional Amounts

Section B

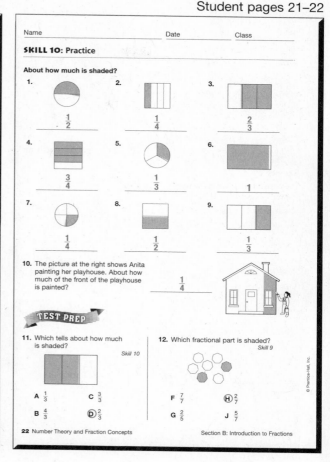

Name _____ Date _____ Class _____

SKILL 10: Estimating Fractional Amounts

You can estimate fractional amounts by imagining the whole being divided into equal parts.

Example 1

About how much of the circle at the right is shaded?

Imagine a line through the middle of the circle dividing it in half as shown.

Since the amount shaded is slightly more than $\frac{1}{2}$ of the circle, you can estimate that about $\frac{1}{2}$ of the circle is shaded.

Example 2

About how much of the figure at the right is shaded?

Imagine lines dividing the rectangle into thirds.

Since the amount shaded is slightly less than $\frac{1}{3}$ of the rectangle, you can estimate that about $\frac{1}{3}$ of the rectangle is shaded.

Guided Practice

1. About how much of the rectangle at the right is shaded?
   a. The lines divide the rectangle into how many equal parts? __4__
   b. About how many parts are shaded? __3__
   c. How much of the rectangle would you estimate is shaded? About $\frac{3}{4}$

2. About how much of the circle at the right is shaded?
   a. The lines divide the circle into how many equal parts? __3__
   b. About how many parts are shaded? __1__
   c. How much of the circle would you estimate is shaded? About $\frac{1}{3}$

Section B: Introduction to Fractions — Number Theory and Fraction Concepts **21**

SKILL 10: Practice

About how much is shaded?

1. $\frac{1}{2}$
2. $\frac{1}{4}$
3. $\frac{2}{3}$
4. $\frac{3}{4}$
5. $\frac{1}{3}$
6. 1
7. $\frac{1}{4}$
8. $\frac{1}{2}$
9. $\frac{1}{3}$

10. The picture at the right shows Anita painting her playhouse. About how much of the front of the playhouse is painted? $\frac{1}{4}$

TEST PREP

11. Which tells about how much is shaded? *Skill 10*

   A $\frac{1}{3}$ C $\frac{3}{3}$
   B $\frac{4}{3}$ D $\frac{2}{3}$

12. Which fractional part is shaded? *Skill 9*

   F $\frac{7}{7}$ H $\frac{2}{7}$
   G $\frac{2}{5}$ J $\frac{5}{7}$

22 Number Theory and Fraction Concepts — Section B: Introduction to Fractions

Objective

Estimate fractional amounts.

 Transparency 5 can be useful with a group of students.

AS STUDENTS WORK...

Guided Practice The goal is not to determine what precise fractional amount is shaded but rather to estimate a commonly used fractional amount, such as $\frac{1}{4}, \frac{1}{3}, \frac{1}{2}, \frac{2}{3}, \frac{3}{4}$, or 1 whole.

Remind students that they have used estimation techniques with whole numbers and with decimals.

Guided Practice Have students use the dashed lines to help them divide each whole into convenient equal parts.

Practice 1–10 Suggest to students that they first determine whether the shaded part is more or less than $\frac{1}{2}$. If it is close, then $\frac{1}{2}$ would be the appropriate estimate. If not, then they need to decide if thirds or fourths are the best way to visualize the whole in equal parts.

Error Alert Many students may have trouble differentiating between an estimate of $\frac{1}{4}$ and $\frac{1}{3}$ and between $\frac{2}{3}$ and $\frac{3}{4}$. Using Transparency 5 can help with this concept.

Error Analysis/Skills Trace

Answer	Work needed	Skill
11 A, B, or C	Estimating a fractional part of a whole	N10
12 F, G, or J	Writing a fraction for part of a set	N9

N = Number Theory and Fraction Concepts

SKILL 11:
Equivalent Fractions

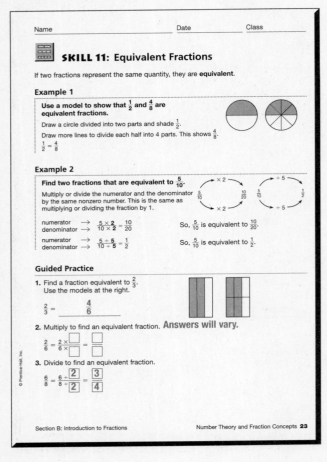

Name _____ Date _____ Class _____

 SKILL 11: Equivalent Fractions

If two fractions represent the same quantity, they are **equivalent**.

Example 1

Use a model to show that $\frac{1}{2}$ and $\frac{4}{8}$ are equivalent fractions.

Draw a circle divided into two parts and shade $\frac{1}{2}$.

Draw more lines to divide each half into 4 parts. This shows $\frac{4}{8}$.

$\frac{1}{2} = \frac{4}{8}$

Example 2

Find two fractions that are equivalent to $\frac{5}{10}$.

Multiply or divide the numerator and the denominator by the same nonzero number. This is the same as multiplying or dividing the fraction by 1.

numerator → $\frac{5 \times 2}{10 \times 2} = \frac{10}{20}$ So, $\frac{5}{10}$ is equivalent to $\frac{10}{20}$.
denominator →

numerator → $\frac{5 \div 5}{10 \div 5} = \frac{1}{2}$ So, $\frac{5}{10}$ is equivalent to $\frac{1}{2}$.
denominator →

Guided Practice

1. Find a fraction equivalent to $\frac{2}{3}$.
   Use the models at the right.

   $\frac{2}{3} = \frac{4}{6}$

2. Multiply to find an equivalent fraction. **Answers will vary.**

   $\frac{2}{6} = \frac{2 \times \square}{6 \times \square} = \frac{\square}{\square}$

3. Divide to find an equivalent fraction.

   $\frac{6}{8} = \frac{6 \div 2}{8 \div 2} = \frac{3}{4}$

© Prentice-Hall, Inc.

Section B: Introduction to Fractions   Number Theory and Fraction Concepts **23**

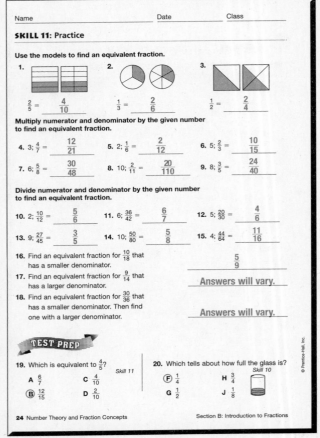

Name _____ Date _____ Class _____

SKILL 11: Practice

Use the models to find an equivalent fraction.

1. $\frac{2}{5} = \frac{4}{10}$ 2. $\frac{1}{3} = \frac{2}{6}$ 3. $\frac{1}{2} = \frac{2}{4}$

Multiply numerator and denominator by the given number to find an equivalent fraction.

4. 3; $\frac{4}{7} = \frac{12}{21}$ 5. 2; $\frac{1}{6} = \frac{2}{12}$ 6. 5; $\frac{2}{3} = \frac{10}{15}$

7. 6; $\frac{5}{8} = \frac{30}{48}$ 8. 10; $\frac{2}{11} = \frac{20}{110}$ 9. 8; $\frac{3}{5} = \frac{24}{40}$

Divide numerator and denominator by the given number to find an equivalent fraction.

10. 2; $\frac{10}{12} = \frac{5}{6}$ 11. 6; $\frac{36}{42} = \frac{6}{7}$ 12. 5; $\frac{20}{30} = \frac{4}{6}$

13. 9; $\frac{27}{45} = \frac{3}{5}$ 14. 10; $\frac{50}{80} = \frac{5}{8}$ 15. 4; $\frac{44}{64} = \frac{11}{16}$

16. Find an equivalent fraction for $\frac{10}{18}$ that has a smaller denominator. $\frac{5}{9}$

17. Find an equivalent fraction for $\frac{9}{14}$ that has a larger denominator.   **Answers will vary.**

18. Find an equivalent fraction for $\frac{30}{36}$ that has a smaller denominator. Then find one with a larger denominator.   **Answers will vary.**

TEST PREP

19. Which is equivalent to $\frac{4}{5}$?   *Skill 11*
   A $\frac{6}{7}$ C $\frac{4}{10}$
   B $\frac{12}{15}$ D $\frac{2}{10}$

20. Which tells about how full the glass is?   *Skill 10*
   F $\frac{1}{4}$ H $\frac{3}{4}$
   G $\frac{1}{2}$ J $\frac{1}{8}$

© Prentice-Hall, Inc.

24 Number Theory and Fraction Concepts   Section B: Introduction to Fractions

---

Objective

Write equivalent fractions.

 **Transparency 6** can be useful with a group of students.

AS STUDENTS WORK...

Guided Practice 1 Have students identify the number of equal parts in the first rectangle and then how many are shaded. Be sure they see that the fraction $\frac{2}{3}$ represents this amount. Then have them tell the number of equal parts in the second rectangle and how many are shaded. After naming the second rectangle's shaded parts with a fraction, point out that the shaded regions are the same size, or equivalent.

Guided Practice 2 and 3 Emphasize that students must multiply or divide the numerator and the denominator by the *same* number.

Practice 4–15 Be sure students understand they are to multiply or divide the numerator and denominator of each fraction by the given number.

Practice 16 The only possible answer is $\frac{5}{9}$.

Error Alert Students often do not multiply or divide the numerator and the denominator by the *same* number.

TEST PREP

Error Analysis/Skills Trace

Answer	Work needed	Skill
19 A, C, or D	Identifying equivalent fractions	N11
20 G, H, or J	Estimating a fractional part of a whole	N10

N = Number Theory and Fraction Concepts

SKILL 12:
Simplest Form

Student pages 25–26

Name _____ Date _____ Class _____

 SKILL 12: Simplest Form

A fraction is in simplest form when the only common factor of the numerator and the denominator is 1.

Example 1

Write $\frac{8}{24}$ in simplest form.

Divide the numerator and the denominator by a common factor.	→	Continue dividing if there are still common factors (other than 1).	→	The fraction is in simplest form because the only common factor of 1 and 3 is 1.
$\frac{8 \div 2}{24 \div 2} = \frac{4}{12}$		$\frac{4 \div 4}{12 \div 4} = \frac{1}{3}$		$\frac{8}{24} = \frac{1}{3}$
not in simplest form		in simplest form		

Example 2

Write $\frac{36}{42}$ in simplest form.

To write a fraction in simplest form, you can divide the numerator and the denominator by their greatest common factor (GCF).

Factors of 36: **1, 2, 3**, 4, **6**, 9, 12, 18, 36

Factors of 42: **1, 2, 3, 6**, 7, 14, 21, 42

The GCF is 6.

$\frac{36}{42} = \frac{36 \div 6}{42 \div 6} = \frac{6}{7}$

$\frac{6}{7}$ is in simplest form.

Guided Practice

1. Write $\frac{4}{10}$ in simplest form.

   a. What is the GCF of 4 and 10? __2__

   b. Divide numerator and denominator by your answer to part **a**.

   $\frac{4 \div \boxed{2}}{10 \div \boxed{2}} = \frac{\boxed{2}}{\boxed{5}}$

2. Write $\frac{32}{40}$ in simplest form. ___$\frac{4}{5}$___

Section B: Introduction to Fractions   Number Theory and Fraction Concepts **25**

Name _____ Date _____ Class _____

SKILL 12: Practice

Find the GCF of the numerator and denominator in each fraction. Then write the fraction in simplest form.

1. $\frac{6}{9}$ 2. $\frac{10}{40}$ 3. $\frac{28}{48}$

  GCF: __3__   GCF: __10__   GCF: __4__

  Simplest form: $\frac{2}{3}$ Simplest form: $\frac{1}{4}$ Simplest form: $\frac{7}{12}$

Write in simplest form.

4. $\frac{12}{24}$ $\frac{1}{2}$ 5. $\frac{9}{21}$ $\frac{3}{7}$ 6. $\frac{8}{10}$ $\frac{4}{5}$ 7. $\frac{6}{28}$ $\frac{3}{14}$

8. $\frac{18}{20}$ $\frac{9}{10}$ 9. $\frac{30}{38}$ $\frac{15}{19}$ 10. $\frac{8}{20}$ $\frac{2}{5}$ 11. $\frac{12}{18}$ $\frac{2}{3}$

12. $\frac{14}{32}$ $\frac{7}{16}$ 13. $\frac{8}{12}$ $\frac{2}{3}$ 14. $\frac{12}{16}$ $\frac{3}{4}$ 15. $\frac{12}{30}$ $\frac{2}{5}$

16. $\frac{9}{15}$ $\frac{3}{5}$ 17. $\frac{6}{42}$ $\frac{1}{7}$ 18. $\frac{9}{12}$ $\frac{3}{4}$ 19. $\frac{6}{15}$ $\frac{2}{5}$

20. $\frac{6}{10}$ $\frac{3}{5}$ 21. $\frac{6}{12}$ $\frac{1}{2}$ 22. $\frac{24}{30}$ $\frac{4}{5}$ 23. $\frac{21}{28}$ $\frac{3}{4}$

24. $\frac{14}{24}$ $\frac{7}{12}$ 25. $\frac{36}{48}$ $\frac{3}{4}$ 26. $\frac{16}{52}$ $\frac{4}{13}$ 27. $\frac{18}{81}$ $\frac{2}{9}$

28. A kilometer is about $\frac{6}{10}$ of a mile. Write this fraction in simplest form. $\frac{3}{5}$

29. Last week, $\frac{25}{30}$ of the students in Mr. Lim's class went on a field trip. Write this fraction in simplest form. $\frac{5}{6}$

30. The band members make up $\frac{35}{100}$ students at Winfield Middle School. Write this fraction in simplest form. $\frac{7}{20}$

TEST PREP

31. Which is in simplest form?   *Skill 12*

   Ⓐ $\frac{9}{16}$ C $\frac{9}{18}$

   B $\frac{6}{15}$ D $\frac{8}{14}$

32. Which is equivalent to $\frac{5}{8}$?   *Skill 11*

   F $\frac{6}{10}$ H $\frac{3}{4}$

   G $\frac{10}{14}$ Ⓙ $\frac{20}{32}$

26 Number Theory and Fraction Concepts   Section B: Introduction to Fractions

---

Objective

Write fractions in simplest form.

 **Transparency 6** can be useful with a group of students.

AS STUDENTS WORK...

Guided Practice Emphasize that students may be able to divide the numerator and denominator by more than one common factor.

You may wish to introduce the idea of using the greatest common factor (GCF) from Skill 6. However, point out that the simplest form can be found by dividing by any common factor that is convenient. The important concept is that when in simplest form, there are no common factors greater than 1 in the numerator and the denominator.

Practice Remind students that they must divide both numerator and denominator by the same factor.

Stress that they check to see that no more common factors remain before writing their final answer.

Error Alert Students often partially simplify a fraction, but not completely. Use Exercise 4 as an example. $\frac{12}{24}$ can be simplified to $\frac{2}{4}, \frac{3}{6}, \frac{4}{8}$, and $\frac{6}{12}$, but the *simplest* form is $\frac{1}{2}$.

TEST PREP

Error Analysis/Skills Trace

Answer	Work needed	Skill
31 B, C, or D	Writing fractions in simplest form	N12
32 F, G, or H	Identifying equivalent fractions	N11

N = Number Theory and Fraction Concepts

Section B: Introduction to Fractions   Number Theory and Fraction Concepts **17**

SKILL 13: Writing Fractions with the Least Common Denominator

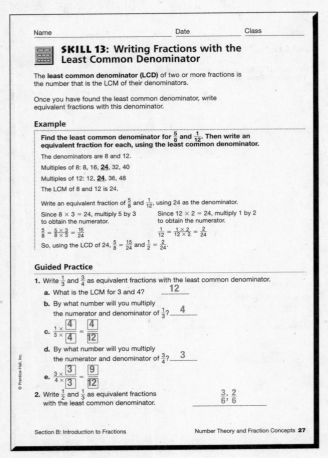

SKILL 13: Writing Fractions with the Least Common Denominator

The **least common denominator (LCD)** of two or more fractions is the number that is the LCM of their denominators.

Once you have found the least common denominator, write equivalent fractions with this denominator.

Example

Find the least common denominator for $\frac{5}{8}$ and $\frac{1}{12}$. Then write an equivalent fraction for each, using the least common denominator.

The denominators are 8 and 12.

Multiples of 8: 8, 16, **24**, 32, 40

Multiples of 12: 12, **24**, 36, 48

The LCM of 8 and 12 is 24.

Write an equivalent fraction of $\frac{5}{8}$ and $\frac{1}{12}$, using 24 as the denominator.

Since $8 \times 3 = 24$, multiply 5 by 3 to obtain the numerator.

$\frac{5}{8} = \frac{5 \times 3}{8 \times 3} = \frac{15}{24}$

Since $12 \times 2 = 24$, multiply 1 by 2 to obtain the numerator.

$\frac{1}{12} = \frac{1 \times 2}{12 \times 2} = \frac{2}{24}$

So, using the LCD of 24, $\frac{5}{8} = \frac{15}{24}$ and $\frac{1}{2} = \frac{2}{24}$.

Guided Practice

1. Write $\frac{1}{3}$ and $\frac{3}{4}$ as equivalent fractions with the least common denominator.

a. What is the LCM for 3 and 4? **12**

b. By what number will you multiply the numerator and denominator of $\frac{1}{3}$? **4**

c. $\frac{1 \times \boxed{4}}{3 \times \boxed{4}} = \frac{\boxed{4}}{\boxed{12}}$

d. By what number will you multiply the numerator and denominator of $\frac{3}{4}$? **3**

e. $\frac{3 \times \boxed{3}}{4 \times \boxed{3}} = \frac{\boxed{9}}{\boxed{12}}$

2. Write $\frac{1}{2}$ and $\frac{1}{3}$ as equivalent fractions with the least common denominator. $\frac{3}{6}, \frac{2}{6}$

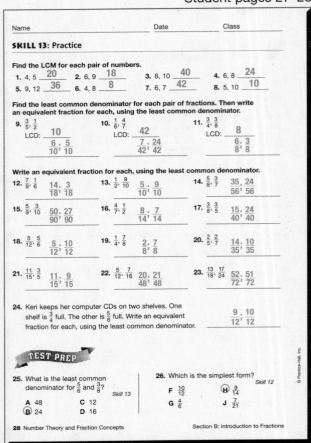

SKILL 13: Practice

Find the LCM for each pair of numbers.

1. 4, 5 **20**   2. 6, 9 **18**   3. 8, 10 **40**   4. 6, 8 **24**

5. 9, 12 **36**   6. 4, 8 **8**   7. 6, 7 **42**   8. 5, 10 **10**

Find the least common denominator for each pair of fractions. Then write an equivalent fraction for each, using the least common denominator.

9. $\frac{3}{5}, \frac{1}{2}$ LCD: **10** $\frac{6}{10}, \frac{5}{10}$

10. $\frac{1}{6}, \frac{4}{7}$ LCD: **42** $\frac{7}{42}, \frac{24}{42}$

11. $\frac{3}{4}, \frac{3}{8}$ LCD: **8** $\frac{6}{8}, \frac{3}{8}$

Write an equivalent fraction for each, using the least common denominator.

12. $\frac{7}{9}, \frac{1}{6}$ $\frac{14}{18}, \frac{3}{18}$

13. $\frac{1}{2}, \frac{9}{10}$ $\frac{5}{10}, \frac{9}{10}$

14. $\frac{5}{8}, \frac{3}{7}$ $\frac{35}{56}, \frac{24}{56}$

15. $\frac{5}{9}, \frac{3}{10}$ $\frac{50}{90}, \frac{27}{90}$

16. $\frac{4}{7}, \frac{1}{2}$ $\frac{8}{14}, \frac{7}{14}$

17. $\frac{3}{8}, \frac{3}{5}$ $\frac{15}{40}, \frac{24}{40}$

18. $\frac{5}{12}, \frac{5}{6}$ $\frac{5}{12}, \frac{10}{12}$

19. $\frac{1}{4}, \frac{7}{8}$ $\frac{2}{8}, \frac{7}{8}$

20. $\frac{2}{5}, \frac{2}{7}$ $\frac{14}{35}, \frac{10}{35}$

21. $\frac{11}{15}, \frac{3}{5}$ $\frac{11}{15}, \frac{9}{15}$

22. $\frac{5}{12}, \frac{7}{16}$ $\frac{20}{48}, \frac{21}{48}$

23. $\frac{13}{18}, \frac{17}{24}$ $\frac{52}{72}, \frac{51}{72}$

24. Keri keeps her computer CDs on two shelves. One shelf is $\frac{3}{4}$ full. The other is $\frac{5}{6}$ full. Write an equivalent fraction for each, using the least common denominator. $\frac{9}{12}, \frac{10}{12}$

 **TEST PREP**

25. What is the least common denominator for $\frac{5}{6}$ and $\frac{3}{2}$? *Skill 13*

A 48   C 12
Ⓑ 24   D 16

26. Which is the simplest form? *Skill 12*

F $\frac{10}{12}$ Ⓗ $\frac{9}{14}$
G $\frac{4}{6}$ J $\frac{7}{21}$

Objective

Write fractions with the least common denominator.

 Transparency 6 can be useful with a group of students.

AS STUDENTS WORK...

Guided Practice 1 Stress that the goal is to find equivalent fractions for each of the two original fractions.

Help students see that the least common denominator will be the least common multiple (LCM) of the original denominators.

Emphasize that they must multiply the numerator and the denominator of a fraction by the same number.

Practice 1–8 Refer students to Skill 7 if they have difficulty finding the LCM.

Practice 9–24 Remind students that they need to determine the appropriate factor to multiply by to create equivalent fractions.

Error Alert Students may change the denominators of the fractions to the correct LCD, but may forget to change the numerators appropriately. Transparency 6 on equivalent fractions can be used to remind them that the new form for each fraction must be equivalent to the original.

TEST PREP

Error Analysis/Skills Trace

Answer	Work needed	Skill
25 A, C, or D	Writing equivalent fractions with the LCD	N13
26 F, G, or J	Writing fractions in simplest form	N12

N = Number Theory and Fraction Concepts

Test Prep and Mixed Review for Section B

Section B

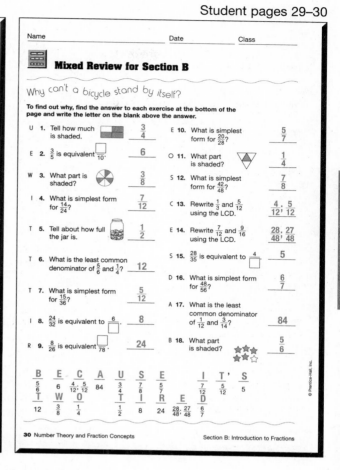

Name _____ **Date** _____ **Class** _____

TEST PREP FOR SECTION B

Circle each correct answer.

1. Which is equivalent to $\frac{3}{8}$? *Skill 11*

A $\frac{6}{8}$ C $\frac{3}{4}$
B $\frac{9}{24}$ D $\frac{3}{16}$

2. Which shows the shaded part? *Skill 9*

F $\frac{1}{4}$ H $\frac{4}{4}$
G $\frac{1}{3}$ J $\frac{3}{4}$

3. Which is in simplest form? *Skill 12*

A $\frac{4}{9}$ C $\frac{4}{6}$
B $\frac{3}{6}$ D $\frac{10}{12}$

4. Which tells about how much is shaded? *Skill 10*

F $\frac{2}{3}$ H $\frac{1}{2}$
G $\frac{3}{4}$ J $\frac{9}{10}$

5. What is the least common denominator for $\frac{2}{5}$ and $\frac{1}{3}$? *Skill 13*

A 3   C 15
B 5   D 30

6. Which is in simplest form? *Skill 12*

F $\frac{4}{6}$ H $\frac{6}{9}$
G $\frac{4}{12}$ J $\frac{2}{3}$

7. Which shows the shaded part? *Skill 9*

A $\frac{5}{6}$ C $\frac{1}{5}$
B $\frac{1}{5}$ D $\frac{5}{1}$

8. Which is equivalent to $\frac{30}{36}$? *Skill 11*

F $\frac{18}{15}$ H $\frac{10}{12}$
G $\frac{4}{6}$ J $\frac{24}{30}$

9. Which tells about how full the jar is? *Skill 10*

A $\frac{2}{3}$ C $\frac{1}{2}$
B $\frac{3}{4}$ D $\frac{1}{3}$

10. Which shows an equivalent fraction for $\frac{5}{8}$ and an equivalent fraction for $\frac{5}{6}$, using the LCD? *Skill 13*

F $\frac{15}{24}, \frac{20}{24}$ H $\frac{5}{24}, \frac{20}{24}$
G $\frac{30}{48}, \frac{40}{48}$ J $\frac{10}{24}, \frac{20}{24}$

11. Which is equivalent to $\frac{24}{28}$? *Skill 11*

A $\frac{20}{24}$ C $\frac{30}{34}$
B $\frac{12}{14}$ D $\frac{12}{16}$

12. Which shows an equivalent fraction for $\frac{7}{9}$ and an equivalent fraction for $\frac{5}{6}$, using the LCD? *Skill 13*

F $\frac{7}{12}, \frac{10}{12}$ H $\frac{42}{54}, \frac{45}{54}$
G $\frac{14}{18}, \frac{15}{18}$ J $\frac{7}{18}, \frac{5}{18}$

Section B: Introduction to Fractions

Number Theory and Fraction Concepts **29**

© Prentice-Hall, Inc.

Name _____ **Date** _____ **Class** _____

Mixed Review for Section B

Why can't a bicycle stand by itself?

To find out why, find the answer to each exercise at the bottom of the page and write the letter on the blank above the answer.

U **1.** Tell how much is shaded. — $\frac{3}{4}$

E **2.** $\frac{3}{5}$ is equivalent to $\frac{6}{10}$. — 6

W **3.** What part is shaded? — $\frac{3}{8}$

I **4.** What is simplest form for $\frac{14}{24}$? — $\frac{7}{12}$

T **5.** Tell about how full the jar is. — $\frac{1}{2}$

T **6.** What is the least common denominator of $\frac{5}{6}$ and $\frac{1}{4}$? — 12

T **7.** What is simplest form for $\frac{15}{36}$? — $\frac{5}{12}$

I **8.** $\frac{24}{32}$ is equivalent to $\frac{6}{8}$. — 8

R **9.** $\frac{8}{26}$ is equivalent to $\frac{?}{78}$. — 24

E **10.** What is simplest form for $\frac{20}{28}$? — $\frac{5}{7}$

O **11.** What part is shaded? — $\frac{1}{4}$

S **12.** What is simplest form for $\frac{42}{48}$? — $\frac{7}{8}$

C **13.** Rewrite $\frac{1}{3}$ and $\frac{5}{12}$ using the LCD. — $\frac{4}{12}, \frac{5}{12}$

E **14.** Rewrite $\frac{7}{12}$ and $\frac{9}{16}$ using the LCD. — $\frac{28}{48}, \frac{27}{48}$

S **15.** $\frac{28}{35}$ is equivalent to $\frac{4}{?}$. — 5

D **16.** What is simplest form for $\frac{48}{56}$? — $\frac{6}{7}$

A **17.** What is the least common denominator of $\frac{1}{2}$ and $\frac{3}{14}$? — 84

B **18.** What part is shaded? — $\frac{5}{6}$

$\underset{\frac{5}{6}}{B}\ \underset{6}{E}\ \underset{\frac{4}{12},\frac{5}{12}}{C}\ \underset{84}{A}\ \underset{\frac{3}{4}}{U}\ \underset{\frac{7}{8}}{S}\ \underset{\frac{5}{7}}{E}\quad \underset{\frac{7}{12}}{I}\ \underset{\frac{5}{12}}{T}\ \underset{5}{S}$

$\underset{12}{T}\ \underset{\frac{3}{8}}{W}\ \underset{\frac{1}{2}}{O}\quad \underset{8}{I}\ \underset{24}{T}\ \underset{\frac{28}{48},\frac{27}{48}}{R}\ \underset{\frac{6}{7}}{E}\ \underset{}{D}$

30 Number Theory and Fraction Concepts

Section B: Introduction to Fractions

© Prentice-Hall, Inc.

TEST PREP

Error Analysis/Skills Trace

Answer	Work needed	Skill
1 A, C, or D	Identifying equivalent fractions	N11
2 F, G, or H	Writing a fraction for part of a whole	N9
3 B, C, or D	Writing fractions in simplest form	N12
4 F, H, or J	Estimating a fractional part of a whole	N10
5 A, B, or D	Writing equivalent fractions with the LCD	N13
6 F, G, or H	Writing fractions in simplest form	N12
7 B, C, or D	Writing a fraction for part of a set	N9
8 F, G, or J	Identifying equivalent fractions	N11
9 A, B, or C	Estimating a fractional part of a whole	N10
10 G, H, or J	Writing equivalent fractions with the LCD	N13
11 A, C, or D	Identifying equivalent fractions	N11
12 F, H, or J	Writing equivalent fractions with the LCD	N13

N = Number Theory and Fraction Concepts

Mixed Review

Error Alert Tell students that once they have provided the answer to an exercise, they are to find that answer at the bottom of the page under a blank. On the blank, they should then write the letter that is to the left of the exercise number. No answer is used more than once.

Section C: Fractions, Mixed Numbers, and Decimals

Math Background

SKILL 14

Stress that an improper fraction is one in which the numerator is greater than or *equal to* the denominator. Many students think that the numerator must be greater than the denominator and do not recognize that a fraction that names 1, such as $\frac{5}{5}$, is considered improper.

When changing mixed numbers to improper fractions, students should recognize that they multiply the number of wholes by the number of equal parts in each whole. In other words, to find how many thirds there are in the 4 wholes in the mixed number $4\frac{2}{3}$, multiply 3×4.

SKILL 15

Students need to recognize that one meaning of a fraction is to indicate the operation of division. It is important in this lesson for students to understand why the remainder is written over the divisor to form the fractional part of a mixed number quotient. The remainder refers to how many parts of a whole are "extra."

SKILL 16

It is essential that students understand that they must compare parts of equal size. If the fractions to be compared do not have common denominators, they will need to write them with the LCD.

When ordering fractions, students must first change all fractions to equivalent

fractions with the LCD. Then they need only pay attention to ordering the numerators appropriately.

SKILL 17

Decimals are a way to represent fractions that have denominators of 10, 100, 1000, and so on. Both fractions and decimals can be used to express part of a whole. Students need to be comfortable with writing both a fraction and a decimal for a model.

SKILL 18

The division meaning of a fraction is extended to include quotients that are decimals rather than whole or mixed numbers. If the decimal representation for a fraction does not terminate, then it is a repeating decimal.

Transparencies

Transparency 7 can be used to help students understand how to compare and order fractions.

Transparency 8 can be used to help students represent a model with both a fraction and a decimal.

Use with Skill 16.

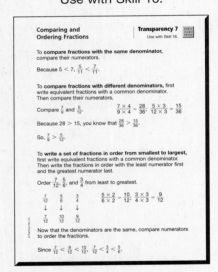

Use with Skill 17.

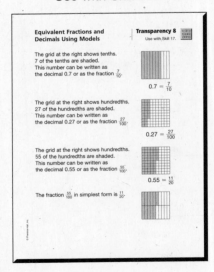

SKILL 14:
Improper Fractions and Mixed Numbers

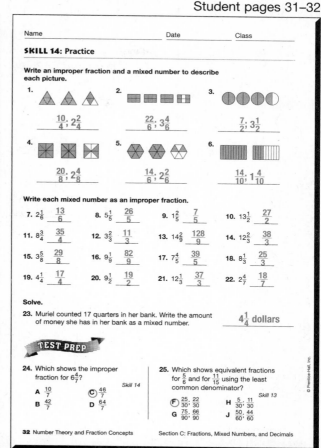

Name _____ Date _____ Class _____

SKILL 14: Improper Fractions and Mixed Numbers

An improper fraction has a numerator that is greater than or equal to its denominator. So, it has a value greater than or equal to 1. A mixed number shows the sum of a whole number and a fraction.

Example 1

Write an improper fraction and a mixed number to describe the picture at the right.

The shapes are divided into fifths, so the denominator of the fraction will be 5. There are 12 shaded parts, so the numerator will be 12.

$\frac{12}{5}$ ← 12 shaded parts / ← all parts are fifths

There are 2 wholes shaded.
The third shape has 2 fifths shaded.

two wholes → $2\frac{2}{5}$ ← 2 shaded parts / ← all parts are fifths

The improper fraction $\frac{12}{5}$ and the mixed number $2\frac{2}{5}$ are equivalent.

Example 2

Write $3\frac{1}{4}$ as an improper fraction.

Step 1: Multiply the denominator by the whole number.

$12 + 1 = 13$

Step 2: Add the numerator.

Step 3: Use the sum from Step 2 as the numerator of the improper fraction. Use the denominator of the fraction.

$3\frac{1}{4}$

So, $3\frac{1}{4} = \frac{13}{4}$. The improper fraction is $\frac{13}{4}$.

$4 \times 3 = 12$

Guided Practice

1. Write an improper fraction and a mixed number to describe the picture at the right. $\frac{16}{7}$, $2\frac{2}{7}$

2. Write $3\frac{4}{5}$ as an improper fraction.
   a. How many fifths are in 3 wholes? __15__
   b. How many total fifths? __19__
   c. Improper fraction: $\frac{19}{5}$

Section C: Fractions, Mixed Numbers, and Decimals   Number Theory and Fraction Concepts **31**

Name _____ Date _____ Class _____

SKILL 14: Practice

Write an improper fraction and a mixed number to describe each picture.

1. $\frac{10}{4}$, $2\frac{2}{4}$
2. $\frac{22}{6}$, $3\frac{4}{6}$
3. $\frac{7}{2}$, $3\frac{1}{2}$
4. $\frac{20}{8}$, $2\frac{4}{8}$
5. $\frac{14}{6}$, $2\frac{2}{6}$
6. $\frac{14}{10}$, $1\frac{4}{10}$

Write each mixed number as an improper fraction.

7. $2\frac{1}{6}$ $\frac{13}{6}$
8. $5\frac{1}{5}$ $\frac{26}{5}$
9. $1\frac{2}{5}$ $\frac{7}{5}$
10. $13\frac{1}{2}$ $\frac{27}{2}$
11. $8\frac{3}{4}$ $\frac{35}{4}$
12. $3\frac{2}{3}$ $\frac{11}{3}$
13. $14\frac{2}{9}$ $\frac{128}{9}$
14. $12\frac{2}{3}$ $\frac{38}{3}$
15. $3\frac{5}{8}$ $\frac{29}{8}$
16. $9\frac{1}{9}$ $\frac{82}{9}$
17. $7\frac{4}{5}$ $\frac{39}{5}$
18. $8\frac{1}{3}$ $\frac{25}{3}$
19. $4\frac{1}{4}$ $\frac{17}{4}$
20. $9\frac{1}{2}$ $\frac{19}{2}$
21. $12\frac{1}{3}$ $\frac{37}{3}$
22. $2\frac{4}{7}$ $\frac{18}{7}$

Solve.

23. Muriel counted 17 quarters in her bank. Write the amount of money she has in her bank as a mixed number. $4\frac{1}{4}$ dollars

24. Which shows the improper fraction for $6\frac{4}{7}$?   *Skill 14*

   A $\frac{10}{7}$ C $\frac{46}{7}$

   B $\frac{42}{7}$ D $\frac{64}{7}$

25. Which shows equivalent fractions for $\frac{5}{6}$ and for $\frac{11}{15}$ using the least common denominator?   *Skill 13*

   F $\frac{25}{30}, \frac{22}{30}$ H $\frac{5}{30}, \frac{11}{30}$

   G $\frac{75}{90}, \frac{66}{90}$ J $\frac{50}{60}, \frac{44}{60}$

32 Number Theory and Fraction Concepts   Section C: Fractions, Mixed Numbers, and Decimals

---

Objective

Write improper fractions as mixed numbers and mixed numbers as improper fractions.

AS STUDENTS WORK...

Guided Practice 1 Ask how many equal parts are in each whole. [7] Help students to see that 7 will be the denominator in both the improper fraction and in the fraction part of the mixed number. Ask how many parts are shaded. [16] Have students write the improper fraction to tell the total number of parts that are shaded. Then have them write the mixed number for the same number of shaded parts.

Guided Practice 2 After answering parts **a** and **b**, ask students what the denominator will be. [5]

Practice 1–6 If students are having difficulty, have them write the mixed numbers for all the exercises, then go back and write the improper fractions.

Error Alert When changing a mixed number to an improper fraction, some students may multiply the denominator and the whole number, then multiply that product by the numerator. After they have multiplied the denominator and the whole number, ask *how many more parts* there are to indicate that addition is the next operation.

TEST PREP

Error Analysis/Skills Trace

Answer	Work needed	Skill
24 A, B, or D	Writing an improper fraction for a mixed number	N14
25 G, H, or J	Writing equivalent fractions with the LCD	N13

Skill Intervention Kit units that are referenced above:

N = Number Theory and Fraction Concepts

SKILL 15: Improper Fractions, Quotients, and Mixed Numbers

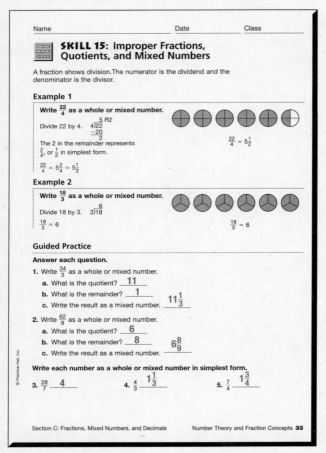

Name _____ **Date** _____ **Class** _____

SKILL 15: Improper Fractions, Quotients, and Mixed Numbers

A fraction shows division. The numerator is the dividend and the denominator is the divisor.

Example 1

Write $\frac{22}{4}$ as a whole or mixed number.

Divide 22 by 4. $4\overline{)22}$ 5 R2
$\;\;\;\;\underline{-20}$
$\;\;\;\;\;\;2$

The 2 in the remainder represents $\frac{2}{4}$, or $\frac{1}{2}$ in simplest form.

$\frac{22}{4} = 5\frac{2}{4} = 5\frac{1}{2}$

$\frac{22}{4} = 5\frac{1}{2}$

Example 2

Write $\frac{18}{3}$ as a whole or mixed number.

Divide 18 by 3. $3\overline{)18}$ 6

$\frac{18}{3} = 6$

$\frac{18}{3} = 6$

Guided Practice

Answer each question.

1. Write $\frac{34}{3}$ as a whole or mixed number.
   a. What is the quotient? __11__
   b. What is the remainder? __1__
   c. Write the result as a mixed number. __$11\frac{1}{3}$__

2. Write $\frac{62}{9}$ as a whole or mixed number.
   a. What is the quotient? __6__
   b. What is the remainder? __8__
   c. Write the result as a mixed number. __$6\frac{8}{9}$__

Write each number as a whole or mixed number in simplest form.

3. $\frac{28}{7}$ __4__
4. $\frac{4}{3}$ __$1\frac{1}{3}$__
5. $\frac{7}{4}$ __$1\frac{3}{4}$__

Section C: Fractions, Mixed Numbers, and Decimals   Number Theory and Fraction Concepts **33**

Name _____ **Date** _____ **Class** _____

SKILL 15: Practice

Write each fraction as a whole or mixed number. Express fractions in simplest form.

1. $\frac{30}{6}$ __5__
2. $\frac{43}{7}$ __$6\frac{1}{7}$__
3. $\frac{14}{7}$ __2__
4. $\frac{24}{6}$ __4__
5. $\frac{32}{16}$ __2__
6. $\frac{48}{8}$ __6__
7. $\frac{72}{9}$ __8__
8. $\frac{80}{10}$ __8__
9. $\frac{16}{5}$ __$3\frac{1}{5}$__
10. $\frac{56}{7}$ __8__
11. $\frac{90}{9}$ __10__
12. $\frac{68}{11}$ __$6\frac{2}{11}$__
13. $\frac{76}{12}$ __$6\frac{1}{3}$__
14. $\frac{45}{5}$ __9__
15. $\frac{38}{19}$ __2__
16. $\frac{88}{10}$ __$8\frac{4}{5}$__
17. $\frac{122}{11}$ __$11\frac{1}{11}$__
18. $\frac{96}{6}$ __16__
19. $\frac{144}{12}$ __12__
20. $\frac{56}{3}$ __$18\frac{2}{3}$__
21. $\frac{39}{9}$ __$4\frac{1}{3}$__
22. $\frac{120}{8}$ __15__
23. $\frac{87}{4}$ __29__ [note: $\frac{87}{3}$ = 29]
24. $\frac{67}{4}$ __$16\frac{3}{4}$__
25. $\frac{94}{3}$ __$31\frac{1}{3}$__
26. $\frac{135}{9}$ __15__
27. $\frac{91}{7}$ __13__

Show each dinosaur measurement as a mixed number.

28. A geranosaurus was $\frac{6}{5}$ m long.   __$1\frac{1}{5}$m__
29. Each arm of a deinocherius was $\frac{17}{2}$ ft long.   __$8\frac{1}{2}$ft__
30. A hypsilophodon was $\frac{23}{10}$ m long.   __$2\frac{3}{10}$m__

31. Write $\frac{31}{7}$ as a whole or mixed number.   *Skill 15*
   A 4
   B $3\frac{4}{7}$
   C $\frac{4}{7}$
   (D) $4\frac{3}{7}$

32. Which shows the mixed number for $\frac{53}{7}$?   *Skill 14*
   F $8\frac{4}{7}$
   (G) $7\frac{4}{7}$
   H $7\frac{5}{7}$
   J $6\frac{11}{7}$

34 Number Theory and Fraction Concepts   Section C: Fractions, Mixed Numbers, and Decimals

---

Objective

Use the division meaning of a fraction.

AS STUDENTS WORK...

Guided Practice 1 and 2 In Guided Practice 1, after students have found the remainder in part **b**, ask what that remainder means. [There is 1 more *third* left.] Remind them that this means the denominator of the fraction part of the mixed number will be 3. Repeat for Guided Practice 2.

Practice 1–27 In some exercises, students will need to simplify the fraction part of their mixed number answers. Use Exercise 13 as an example. After dividing, students should have $6\frac{4}{12}$ as their answer. Point out that $\frac{4}{12}$ can be written in simplest form as $\frac{1}{3}$. Review Skill 12 for students having trouble reducing the fraction part of their answers.

Error Alert Many students forget to include the fraction part of the answer after dividing. For students having difficulty with this, have them show the division for the fraction $\frac{7}{3}$ by drawing three identical circles each divided into thirds. Have them shade seven of the thirds. Ask how many whole circles are shaded. [2] Have students write 2 for the whole number part of their answer. Then ask how many parts are left. [1] Have them write $\frac{1}{3}$ for the fraction part.

TEST PREP

Error Analysis/Skills Trace

Answer	Work needed	Skill
31 A, B, or C	Using the quotient meaning of a fraction	N15
32 F, H, or J	Writing a mixed number for an improper fraction	N14

N = Number Theory and Fraction Concepts

SKILL 16: Comparing and Ordering Fractions and Mixed Numbers

Student Page 35

Name _____ Date _____ Class _____

SKILL 16: Comparing and Ordering Fractions and Mixed Numbers

When ordering mixed numbers, first order using the whole number part. However, sometimes it is necessary to compare or order fractions. One way to do this is to write each fraction with a common denominator.

Example 1

Compare $\frac{3}{4}$ and $\frac{5}{6}$.

To compare the fractions, write them with a common denominator.

$\frac{3}{4}$ $\frac{5}{6}$

Multiples of 4: 4, 8, **12**, 16
Multiples of 6: 6, **12**, 18, 24

$\rightarrow \frac{9}{12} < \frac{10}{12} \leftarrow$

Since the denominators are the same, compare the numerators.

The least common denominator of 4 and 6 is 12. Using the LCD, write eqivalent fractions.

$9 < 10$, so $\frac{3}{4} < \frac{5}{6}$.

Example 2

Write the mixed numbers $2\frac{5}{8}$, $2\frac{3}{4}$, and $2\frac{7}{10}$ in order from least to greatest.

Multiples of 8: 8, 16, 24, 32, **40**
Multiples of 4: 4, 8, 12, 16, 20, 24, 28, 32, 36, **40**
Multiples of 10: 10, 20, 30, **40**

$\frac{5}{8}$ $\frac{3}{4}$ $\frac{7}{10}$
$\downarrow$ $\downarrow$ $\downarrow$
$\frac{25}{40}$ $\frac{30}{40}$ $\frac{28}{40}$

The least common denominator for 8, 4, and 10 is 40. Write eqivalent fractions.

$25 < 28 < 30$, so the order of the mixed numbers is $2\frac{5}{8}$, $2\frac{7}{10}$, $2\frac{3}{4}$.

Guided Practice

1. Compare $5\frac{1}{4}$ and $5\frac{1}{6}$.

   a. What is the least common denominator? __12__

   b. Write equivalent fractions using the least common denominator. $\frac{3}{12}, \frac{2}{12}$

   c. Compare. $5\frac{1}{4} \;\boxed{>}\; 5\frac{1}{6}$

2. Order $1\frac{5}{6}$, $1\frac{3}{4}$, and $1\frac{3}{5}$ from least to greatest.

   a. Write equivalent fractions using the LCD. $\frac{50}{60}, \frac{45}{60}, \frac{36}{60}$

   b. Order the mixed numbers. $1\frac{3}{5}, 1\frac{3}{4}, 1\frac{5}{6}$

Section C: Fractions, Mixed Numbers, and Decimals   Number Theory and Fraction Concepts **35**

Student Page 36

Name _____ Date _____ Class _____

SKILL 16: Practice

Compare using <, >, or =.

1. $\frac{3}{12} \bigcirc \frac{5}{12}$ 2. $\frac{2}{3} \bigcirc \frac{1}{2}$ 3. $\frac{5}{8} \bigcirc \frac{3}{8}$ 4. $\frac{4}{5} \bigcirc \frac{9}{10}$

5. $\frac{2}{4} \bigcirc \frac{10}{20}$ 6. $\frac{1}{4} \bigcirc \frac{4}{13}$ 7. $\frac{5}{7} \bigcirc \frac{6}{7}$ 8. $\frac{5}{12} \bigcirc \frac{3}{5}$

9. $4\frac{2}{7} \bigcirc 4\frac{1}{7}$ 10. $4\frac{1}{7} \bigcirc 3\frac{3}{18}$ 11. $6\frac{3}{7} \bigcirc 6\frac{4}{9}$

12. $8\frac{4}{6} \bigcirc 8\frac{12}{16}$ 13. $9\frac{2}{6} \bigcirc 9\frac{4}{12}$ 14. $7\frac{5}{6} \bigcirc 6\frac{11}{11}$

Order from least to greatest.

15. $\frac{3}{4}, \frac{3}{5}, \frac{3}{10}$ 16. $3\frac{4}{5}, 3\frac{3}{4}, 3\frac{5}{6}$ 17. $\frac{7}{10}, \frac{18}{25}, \frac{3}{5}$

$\frac{3}{10}, \frac{3}{5}, \frac{3}{4}$ $3\frac{3}{4}, 3\frac{4}{5}, 3\frac{5}{6}$ $\frac{3}{5}, \frac{7}{10}, \frac{18}{25}$

18. $5\frac{1}{5}, 5\frac{1}{6}, 4\frac{7}{30}$ 19. $\frac{33}{100}, \frac{3}{10}, \frac{33}{1,000}$ 20. $\frac{49}{56}, \frac{23}{28}, \frac{12}{14}$

$4\frac{7}{30}, 5\frac{1}{6}, 5\frac{1}{5}$ $\frac{33}{1,000}, \frac{3}{10}, \frac{33}{100}$ $\frac{23}{28}, \frac{12}{14}, \frac{49}{56}$

Solve.

21. Raoul has $2\frac{1}{3}$ cups of milk. Does he have enough to prepare a recipe that uses $2\frac{1}{2}$ cups of milk? __No__

22. Fanelli's Hardware stocks wooden dowels in the following widths: $\frac{3}{16}$ in., $\frac{1}{8}$ in., $\frac{3}{8}$ in., $\frac{1}{4}$ in., $\frac{1}{2}$ in. Write these widths in order from smallest to largest.

$\frac{1}{8}$ in., $\frac{3}{16}$ in., $\frac{1}{4}$ in., $\frac{3}{8}$ in., $\frac{1}{2}$ in.

 **TEST PREP**

23. Which comparison is correct? *Skill 16*

   A $\frac{5}{6} < \frac{3}{5}$ C $\frac{2}{5} > \frac{1}{2}$

   B $\frac{5}{6} > \frac{7}{9}$ D $\frac{8}{9} < \frac{4}{5}$

24. Write $\frac{53}{12}$ as a mixed number. *Skill 15*

   F $4\frac{3}{12}$ H $4\frac{4}{12}$

   G $5\frac{5}{12}$ **J** $4\frac{5}{12}$

36 Number Theory and Fraction Concepts   Section C: Fractions, Mixed Numbers, and Decimals

---

Objective

Compare and order fractions.

 Transparency 7 can be useful with a group of students.

AS STUDENTS WORK...

Guided Practice 2 Ask students if the current denominators are equal. Then ask what denominator could they all be changed to. [60] Remind students that after they have written equivalent fractions in part **a**, they must remember to include the whole numbers in their answer to part **b**.

Practice 1–14 Some students may confuse the use of the < and > symbols. You may want to give them a way to remember the correct use, such as, "The sign always points to the smaller number." Remind students that if the whole numbers are not equal, they only have to compare the whole numbers; they do not have to write equivalent fractions.

Practice 15–20 Watch for students who forget to change the numerators of the fractions when writing equivalent fractions with the LCD.

Error Alert In Exercises 15–20, some students may list the fractions in order from greatest to least. For such students, after they have found equivalent fractions, ask, "Which numerator is the least?" Use this strategy to help them remember to begin with the least fraction.

TEST PREP

Error Analysis/Skills Trace

Answer	Work needed	Skill
23 A, C, or D	Comparing two fractions with unlike denominators	N16
24 F, G, or H	Using the quotient meaning of a fraction	N15

N = Number Theory and Fraction Concepts

SKILL 17: Writing Equivalent Fractions and Decimals

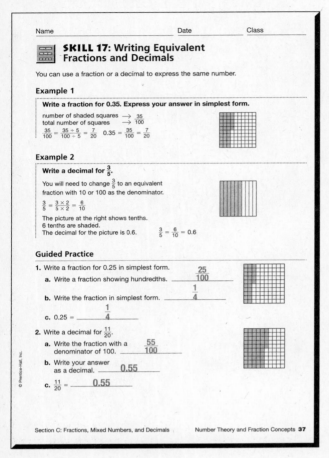

Name _____ Date _____ Class _____

SKILL 17: Writing Equivalent Fractions and Decimals

You can use a fraction or a decimal to express the same number.

Example 1

Write a fraction for 0.35. Express your answer in simplest form.

number of shaded squares → 35
total number of squares → 100

$\frac{35}{100} = \frac{35 \div 5}{100 \div 5} = \frac{7}{20}$ $0.35 = \frac{35}{100} = \frac{7}{20}$

Example 2

Write a decimal for $\frac{3}{5}$.

You will need to change $\frac{3}{5}$ to an equivalent fraction with 10 or 100 as the denominator.

$\frac{3}{5} = \frac{3 \times 2}{5 \times 2} = \frac{6}{10}$

The picture at the right shows tenths.
6 tenths are shaded.
The decimal for the picture is 0.6. $\frac{3}{5} = \frac{6}{10} = 0.6$

Guided Practice

1. Write a fraction for 0.25 in simplest form.
   a. Write a fraction showing hundredths. $\frac{25}{100}$
   b. Write the fraction in simplest form. $\frac{1}{4}$
   c. 0.25 = $\frac{1}{4}$

2. Write a decimal for $\frac{11}{20}$.
   a. Write the fraction with a denominator of 100. $\frac{55}{100}$
   b. Write your answer as a decimal. 0.55
   c. $\frac{11}{20}$ = 0.55

Section C: Fractions, Mixed Numbers, and Decimals   Number Theory and Fraction Concepts **37**

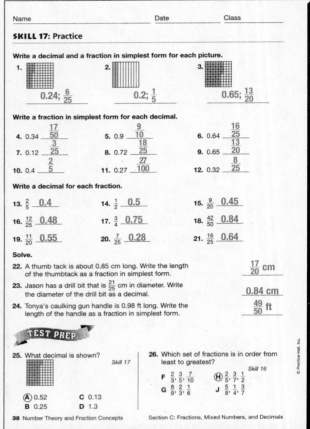

Name _____ Date _____ Class _____

SKILL 17: Practice

Write a decimal and a fraction in simplest form for each picture.

1. 0.24; $\frac{6}{25}$ 2. 0.2; $\frac{1}{5}$ 3. 0.65; $\frac{13}{20}$

Write a fraction in simplest form for each decimal.

4. 0.34 $\frac{17}{50}$ 5. 0.9 $\frac{9}{10}$ 6. 0.64 $\frac{16}{25}$
7. 0.12 $\frac{3}{25}$ 8. 0.72 $\frac{18}{25}$ 9. 0.65 $\frac{13}{20}$
10. 0.4 $\frac{2}{5}$ 11. 0.27 $\frac{27}{100}$ 12. 0.32 $\frac{8}{25}$

Write a decimal for each fraction.

13. $\frac{2}{5}$ 0.4   14. $\frac{1}{2}$ 0.5   15. $\frac{9}{20}$ 0.45
16. $\frac{12}{25}$ 0.48   17. $\frac{3}{4}$ 0.75   18. $\frac{42}{50}$ 0.84
19. $\frac{11}{20}$ 0.55   20. $\frac{7}{25}$ 0.28   21. $\frac{16}{25}$ 0.64

Solve.

22. A thumb tack is about 0.85 cm long. Write the length of the thumbtack as a fraction in simplest form. $\frac{17}{20}$ cm

23. Jason has a drill bit that is $\frac{21}{25}$ cm in diameter. Write the diameter of the drill bit as a decimal. 0.84 cm

24. Tonya's caulking gun handle is 0.98 ft long. Write the length of the handle as a fraction in simplest form. $\frac{49}{50}$ ft

TEST PREP

25. What decimal is shown?   *Skill 17*
    Ⓐ 0.52   C 0.13
    B 0.25   D 1.3

26. Which set of fractions is in order from least to greatest?   *Skill 16*
    F $\frac{2}{3}, \frac{3}{5}, \frac{7}{10}$ Ⓗ $\frac{2}{5}, \frac{3}{7}, \frac{1}{2}$
    G $\frac{8}{9}, \frac{2}{3}, \frac{1}{6}$ J $\frac{5}{8}, \frac{1}{4}, \frac{3}{7}$

38 Number Theory and Fraction Concepts   Section C: Fractions, Mixed Numbers, and Decimals

Objective

Write equivalent fractions and decimals for models.

 Transparency 8 can be useful with a group of students.

AS STUDENTS WORK...

Guided Practice 1 Have students read the decimal out loud: "twenty-five hundredths." Tell them to then write the fraction for what was read.

Guided Practice 2 Have students list the first three multiples of 10: 10, 100, 1000. Ask which of these is the smallest multiple of 20. [100] Write $\frac{11}{20} = \frac{\square}{100}$ and have students complete the equivalent fraction. Remind them that since the denominator is 100, their decimal will have two decimal places.

Practice 4–12 For students having trouble writing the fractions in simplest form, point out that the denominators of 10 and 100 only have factors of 2 and 5. Therefore they should check all numerators for factors of 2 or 5 to reduce.

Error Alert In Practice 13–21, some students may try to use the denominator as part of the decimal form. Remind students to write equivalent fractions with denominators of 10 or 100 only. Then express those fractions in decimal form.

TEST PREP

Error Analysis/Skills Trace

Answer	Work needed	Skill
25 B, C, or D	Writing a decimal for a model	N17
26 F, G, or J	Ordering a set of fractions with unlike denominators	N16

N = Number Theory and Fraction Concepts

SKILL 18: Dividing to Change a Fraction to a Decimal

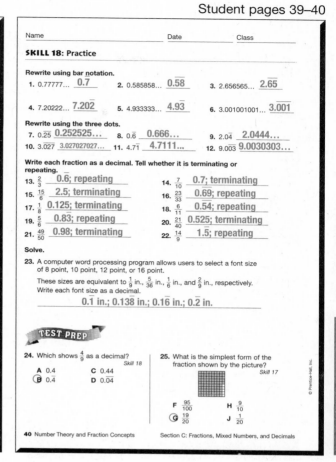

Objective

Divide to change a fraction to a decimal.

AS STUDENTS WORK...

Guided Practice 1 and 2
Provide students with the following examples of repeating decimals shown using both the three dots and the bar: 0.555... and, 0.$\overline{5}$, 0.424242... and 0.$\overline{42}$, 6.123123123... and 6.$\overline{123}$. Emphasize that the three dots mean to continue the pattern shown. The bar only goes over those digits that repeat.

Guided Practice 3 and 4 Ask
students if they get a remainder of 0 when they divide. If so, then the decimal is terminating. If not, then it is repeating.

Practice 13–22 For students having difficulty, review division with decimals from Unit 2. Remind students that the decimal will be placed behind the last digit in the numerator as that is the dividend. The decimal in the quotient will be directly above it. For $\frac{2}{3}$, use $3\overline{)2}$.

Error Alert In Practice 1–12, some students may have difficulty with decimals where not all digits behind the decimal point repeat. Use the following examples.

$0.\overline{042} = 0.042042042...$

$0.0\overline{42} = 0.0424242...$

$0.04\overline{2} = 0.04222...$

Error Analysis/Skills Trace

Answer	Work needed	Skill
24 A, C, or D	Writing a fraction as a decimal	N18
25 F, H, or J	Writing a fraction for a model	N17

N = Number Theory and Fraction Concepts

Test Prep and Mixed Review for Section C

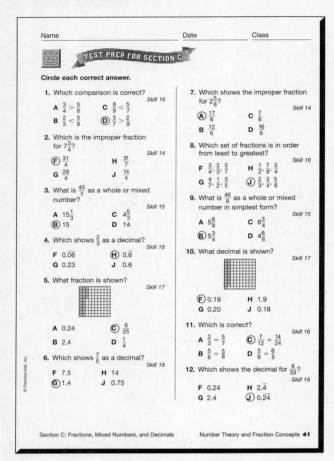

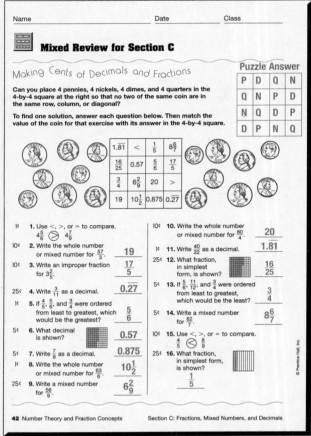

Error Analysis/Skills Trace

Answer	Work needed	Skill
1 A, B, or C	Comparing two fractions with unlike denominators	N16
2 G, H, or J	Writing an improper fraction for a mixed number	N14
3 A, C, or D	Use the quotient meaning of a fraction	N15
4 F, G, or J	Writing a fraction as a decimal	N18
5 A, B, or D	Writing a fraction for a model	N17
6 F, H, or J	Writing a fraction as a decimal	N18
7 B, C, or D	Writing a mixed number for an improper fraction	N14
8 F, G, or H	Ordering a set of fractions with unlike denominators	N16
9 A, C, or D	Using the quotient meaning of a fraction	N15
10 G, H, or J	Writing a decimal for a model	N17
11 A, B, or D	Comparing two fractions with unlike denominators	N16
12 F, G, or H	Writing a fraction as a decimal	N18

N = Number Theory and Fraction Concepts

Mixed Review

Students may want to use small pieces of paper with 1¢, 5¢, 10¢, and 25¢ on them to place over the squares in the picture as they find answers.

Tell students to show repeating decimal answers using the bar.

No answer is used more than once.

POST-TEST A: Number Theory and Fraction Concepts

Section A
Factors and Multiples

1. Which is *not* a factor of 56?

   A 3   **C** 7

   B 2   **D** 8

2. Which is a composite number?

   F 59   **H** 65

   G 37   **J** 43

3. Which is the prime factorization of 54?

   A $2 \times 2 \times 2 \times 7$

   B 2×27

   C 6×9

   D $2 \times 3 \times 3 \times 3$

4. Which is the standard form for 3^3?

   F 27   **H** 6

   G 9   **J** 33

5. Which is the prime factorization for 900 using exponents?

   A $2 + 2 + 3 + 3 + 5 + 5$

   B $2 \times 2 \times 3 \times 3 \times 5 \times 5$

   C $2^2 \times 3^2 \times 5^2$

   D $2^2 \times 3^3 \times 5^2$

6. Which is the GCF of 28 and 48?

   F 12   **H** 2

   G 4   **J** 28

7. Which is the LCM of 16 and 18?

   A 288   **C** 4

   B 144   **D** 2

8. There are 6 protractors in a box and 4 compasses in a box. What is the least number of boxes of compasses that can be purchased to buy the same number of compasses as protractors?

   F 2   **H** 24

   G 12   **J** 3

Section B
Introduction to Fractions

9. Which tells how much is shaded?

   A $\frac{3}{8}$ **C** $\frac{5}{8}$

   B $\frac{3}{5}$ **D** $\frac{5}{3}$

Go On ➡

10. Which tells about how full the pitcher is?

F $\frac{1}{3}$ H $\frac{1}{4}$

G $\frac{1}{2}$ J $\frac{2}{3}$

11. Which is equivalent to $\frac{12}{16}$?

A $\frac{2}{3}$ C $\frac{4}{8}$

B $\frac{9}{10}$ D $\frac{3}{4}$

12. Which is in simplest form?

F $\frac{6}{7}$ H $\frac{9}{15}$

G $\frac{10}{12}$ J $\frac{12}{16}$

13. Which shows equivalent fractions for $\frac{2}{5}$ and for $\frac{1}{4}$ using the LCD?

A $\frac{8}{20}; \frac{5}{20}$ C $\frac{16}{40}; \frac{10}{40}$

B $\frac{4}{20}; \frac{5}{20}$ D $\frac{2}{20}; \frac{1}{20}$

Section C
Fractions, Mixed Numbers, and Decimals

14. Which shows the improper fraction for $6\frac{5}{8}$?

F $\frac{48}{8}$ H $\frac{53}{8}$

G $\frac{11}{8}$ J $\frac{240}{8}$

15. Write $\frac{56}{6}$ as a mixed number in simplest form.

A $9\frac{2}{6}$ C 9

B $9\frac{1}{3}$ D $9\frac{3}{6}$

16. Which is correct?

F $\frac{3}{8} = \frac{9}{16}$ H $\frac{5}{6} > \frac{11}{12}$

G $\frac{2}{5} < \frac{2}{7}$ J $\frac{7}{8} < \frac{9}{10}$

17. Which shows the decimal for the picture?

A 0.20   C 0.24

B 0.25   D 0.30

18. Which shows $\frac{5}{8}$ as a decimal?

F 0.625   H 0.58

G 5.8   J 6.25

Name _____ Date _____ Class _____

 # POST-TEST B: Number Theory and Fraction Concepts

Section A
Factors and Multiples

1. Which is *not* a factor of 36?

   A 4   **C** 8

   B 12   **D** 18

2. Which is a prime number?

   F 69   **H** 24

   G 55   **J** 19

3. Which is the prime factorization of 72?

   A 2×36

   B $2 \times 2 \times 2 \times 3 \times 3$

   C 8×9

   D $2 \times 2 \times 3 \times 3$

4. Which is the standard form for 5^2?

   F 52   **H** 25

   G 10   **J** 55

5. Which is the prime factorization for 540 using exponents?

   A $2 + 2 + 3 + 3 + 3 + 5$

   B $2^3 \times 3^2 \times 5$

   C $2 \times 2 \times 3 \times 3 \times 3 \times 5$

   D $2^2 \times 3^3 \times 5$

6. Which is the GCF of 24 and 36?

   F 12   **H** 4

   G 72   **J** 8

7. Which is the LCM of 15 and 20?

   A 60   **C** 30

   B 300   **D** 40

8. There are 8 flat-head screws in a package and 10 pan-head screws in a package. What is the least number of packages of flat-head screws that can be purchased to buy the same amount of each type of screw?

   F 80   **H** 40

   G 5   **J** 4

Section B
Introduction to Fractions

9. Which tells how much is shaded?

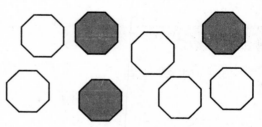

   A $\frac{3}{8}$ **C** $\frac{5}{8}$

   B $\frac{8}{3}$ **D** $\frac{3}{5}$

Go On ➡

10. Which tells about how much is shaded?

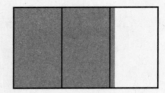

F $\frac{7}{8}$ H $\frac{2}{3}$

G $\frac{1}{3}$ J $\frac{1}{2}$

11. Which is equivalent to $\frac{3}{4}$?

A $\frac{3}{8}$ C $\frac{15}{20}$

B $\frac{9}{16}$ D $\frac{12}{15}$

12. Which is in simplest form?

F $\frac{8}{10}$ H $\frac{8}{16}$

G $\frac{4}{12}$ J $\frac{7}{10}$

13. Which shows equivalent fractions for $\frac{1}{6}$ and $\frac{3}{4}$ using the LCD?

A $\frac{1}{12}; \frac{3}{12}$ C $\frac{4}{24}; \frac{18}{24}$

B $\frac{2}{12}; \frac{9}{12}$ D $\frac{2}{12}; \frac{3}{12}$

Section C
Fractions, Mixed Numbers, and Decimals

14. Which shows the improper fraction for $4\frac{5}{8}$?

F $\frac{37}{8}$ H $\frac{32}{8}$

G $\frac{8}{37}$ J $\frac{29}{8}$

15. Write $\frac{66}{8}$ as a mixed number in simplest form.

A $8\frac{2}{8}$ C 8

B $7\frac{10}{8}$ D $8\frac{1}{4}$

16. Which is correct?

F $\frac{9}{10} < \frac{4}{5}$ H $\frac{3}{5} > \frac{2}{3}$

G $\frac{6}{7} = \frac{18}{21}$ J $\frac{3}{4} > \frac{11}{12}$

17. Which shows the decimal for the picture?

A 0.28   C 0.70

B 0.72   D 0.78

18. Which shows $\frac{5}{6}$ as a decimal?

F 0.833   H $0.8\overline{3}$

G $0.\overline{83}$ J 0.83

Name _____ Date _____ Class _____

 # Number Theory and Fraction Concepts

Student Answer and Assignment Sheet

Which test? Fill in one shape.

☐ △ ◇

Pretest   Post-test A   Post-test B

	Pretest	Post-test A	Post-test B	
1	Ⓐ	Ⓑ	Ⓒ	Ⓓ
2	Ⓕ	Ⓖ	Ⓗ	Ⓙ
3	Ⓐ	Ⓑ	Ⓒ	Ⓓ
4	Ⓕ	Ⓖ	Ⓗ	Ⓙ
5	Ⓐ	Ⓑ	Ⓒ	Ⓓ
6	Ⓕ	Ⓖ	Ⓗ	Ⓙ
7	Ⓐ	Ⓑ	Ⓒ	Ⓓ
8	Ⓕ	Ⓖ	Ⓗ	Ⓙ
9	Ⓐ	Ⓑ	Ⓒ	Ⓓ
10	Ⓕ	Ⓖ	Ⓗ	Ⓙ
11	Ⓐ	Ⓑ	Ⓒ	Ⓓ
12	Ⓕ	Ⓖ	Ⓗ	Ⓙ
13	Ⓐ	Ⓑ	Ⓒ	Ⓓ
14	Ⓕ	Ⓖ	Ⓗ	Ⓙ
15	Ⓐ	Ⓑ	Ⓒ	Ⓓ
16	Ⓕ	Ⓖ	Ⓗ	Ⓙ
17	Ⓐ	Ⓑ	Ⓒ	Ⓓ
18	Ⓕ	Ⓖ	Ⓗ	Ⓙ

■ ▲ ◆

Section	Score	Assignment	
		Book	**Tutorial Software**
A Factors and Multiples (Items 1–8)	___ out of 8	Complete Section A? ☐ Yes	Complete Section A? ☐ Yes
B Introduction to Fractions (Items 9–13)	___ out of 5	Complete Section B? ☐ Yes	Complete Section B? ☐ Yes
C Fractions, Mixed Numbers, and Decimals (Items 14–18)	___ out of 5	Complete Section C? ☐ Yes	Complete Section C? ☐ Yes

Assignment details/comments:

.

_____ needs to complete
student's name

the above assignment by _____.
date

Teacher: _____

Parent/Guardian: _____

Number Theory and Fraction Concepts

Answer Key and Correlation

SCORING INSTRUCTIONS: This page shows the same answers as the Easy-Score Answer Card. Compare correct answers below to responses on the Student Answer and Assignment Sheet.

■ Pretest

1	Ⓐ	**Ⓑ**	Ⓒ	Ⓓ
2	Ⓕ	Ⓖ	**Ⓗ**	Ⓙ
3	**Ⓐ**	Ⓑ	Ⓒ	Ⓓ
4	**Ⓕ**	Ⓖ	Ⓗ	Ⓙ
5	Ⓐ	Ⓑ	**Ⓒ**	Ⓓ
6	Ⓕ	Ⓖ	Ⓗ	**Ⓙ**
7	Ⓐ	Ⓑ	Ⓒ	**Ⓓ**
8	Ⓕ	**Ⓖ**	Ⓗ	Ⓙ
9	Ⓐ	Ⓑ	Ⓒ	**Ⓓ**
10	Ⓕ	Ⓖ	Ⓗ	**Ⓙ**
11	Ⓐ	**Ⓑ**	Ⓒ	Ⓓ
12	**Ⓕ**	Ⓖ	Ⓗ	Ⓙ
13	**Ⓐ**	Ⓑ	Ⓒ	Ⓓ
14	Ⓕ	**Ⓖ**	Ⓗ	Ⓙ
15	Ⓐ	**Ⓑ**	Ⓒ	Ⓓ
16	Ⓕ	Ⓖ	**Ⓗ**	Ⓙ
17	**Ⓐ**	Ⓑ	Ⓒ	Ⓓ
18	Ⓕ	Ⓖ	Ⓗ	**Ⓙ**

Section A: 1–8, Section B: 9–13, Section C: 14–18

▲ Post-test A

1	**Ⓐ**	Ⓑ	Ⓒ	Ⓓ
2	Ⓕ	Ⓖ	**Ⓗ**	Ⓙ
3	Ⓐ	Ⓑ	Ⓒ	**Ⓓ**
4	**Ⓕ**	Ⓖ	Ⓗ	Ⓙ
5	Ⓐ	Ⓑ	**Ⓒ**	Ⓓ
6	Ⓕ	**Ⓖ**	Ⓗ	Ⓙ
7	Ⓐ	**Ⓑ**	Ⓒ	Ⓓ
8	Ⓕ	Ⓖ	Ⓗ	**Ⓙ**
9	Ⓐ	Ⓑ	**Ⓒ**	Ⓓ
10	Ⓕ	**Ⓖ**	Ⓗ	Ⓙ
11	Ⓐ	Ⓑ	Ⓒ	**Ⓓ**
12	**Ⓕ**	Ⓖ	Ⓗ	Ⓙ
13	**Ⓐ**	Ⓑ	Ⓒ	Ⓓ
14	Ⓕ	Ⓖ	**Ⓗ**	Ⓙ
15	Ⓐ	**Ⓑ**	Ⓒ	Ⓓ
16	Ⓕ	Ⓖ	Ⓗ	**Ⓙ**
17	Ⓐ	Ⓑ	**Ⓒ**	Ⓓ
18	**Ⓕ**	Ⓖ	Ⓗ	Ⓙ

♦ Post-test B

1	Ⓐ	Ⓑ	**Ⓒ**	Ⓓ
2	Ⓕ	Ⓖ	Ⓗ	**Ⓙ**
3	Ⓐ	**Ⓑ**	Ⓒ	Ⓓ
4	Ⓕ	Ⓖ	**Ⓗ**	Ⓙ
5	Ⓐ	Ⓑ	Ⓒ	**Ⓓ**
6	**Ⓕ**	Ⓖ	Ⓗ	Ⓙ
7	**Ⓐ**	Ⓑ	Ⓒ	Ⓓ
8	Ⓕ	**Ⓖ**	Ⓗ	Ⓙ
9	**Ⓐ**	Ⓑ	Ⓒ	Ⓓ
10	Ⓕ	Ⓖ	**Ⓗ**	Ⓙ
11	Ⓐ	Ⓑ	**Ⓒ**	Ⓓ
12	Ⓕ	Ⓖ	Ⓗ	**Ⓙ**
13	Ⓐ	**Ⓑ**	Ⓒ	Ⓓ
14	**Ⓕ**	Ⓖ	Ⓗ	Ⓙ
15	Ⓐ	Ⓑ	Ⓒ	**Ⓓ**
16	Ⓕ	**Ⓖ**	Ⓗ	Ⓙ
17	Ⓐ	**Ⓑ**	Ⓒ	Ⓓ
18	Ⓕ	Ⓖ	**Ⓗ**	Ⓙ

■ Pretest   **▲ Post-test A**   **♦ Post-test B**

Correlation

For help with test items	Use
1–8	Section **A** Factors and Multiples
9–13	Section **B** Introduction to Fractions
14–18	Section **C** Fractions, Mixed Numbers, and Decimals

Note: Test item numbers on all tests also correspond to skill numbers. For example, item 4 on each test corresponds to Skill 4.

Teacher _____   Class _____

Number Theory and Fraction Concepts

Class Profile

INSTRUCTIONS: Use this form to summarize test dates and scores for each student. To record assignments, use markings such as the ones shown at the right.

Student	Pretest		Assignment			Post-test A		Post-test B	
	Date	Score	Sec A	Sec B	Sec C	Date	Score	Date	Score
1.									
2.									
3.									
4.									
5.									
6.									
7.									
8.									
9.									
10.									
11.									
12.									
13.									
14.									
15.									
16.									
17.									
18.									
19.									
20.									
21.									
22.									
23.									
24.									
25.									

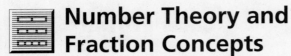

Number Theory and Fraction Concepts

Item Analysis

INSTRUCTIONS: This optional form may be used to record which pretest items each student misses. This would provide a visual means to identify the skills that are most problematic for each student or for the class as a whole. As a way to show student/class improvement, the form may also be used to record the results of post-tests. See examples at the right.

◣ Item missed on Pretest
◤ Item missed on Post-test

Student	Section A								Section B					Section C				
	1	2	3	4	5	6	7	8	9	10	11	12	13	14	15	16	17	18
1.																		
2.																		
3.																		
4.																		
5.																		
6.																		
7.																		
8.																		
9.																		
10.																		
11.																		
12.																		
13.																		
14.																		
15.																		
16.																		
17.																		
18.																		
19.																		
20.																		
21.																		
22.																		
23.																		
24.																		
25.																		

Number Theory and Fraction Concepts

Easy-Score Answer Card

SCORING INSTRUCTIONS: Align the Easy-Score Answer Card over shaded shapes on the Student Answer and Assignment Sheet. Responses that are correct will appear through the holes.

Pretest ■

Post-test A ▲

Post-test B ◆

Pretest

Section A

1. Ⓐ ● Ⓒ Ⓓ
2. Ⓕ Ⓖ ● Ⓙ
3. ● Ⓑ Ⓒ Ⓓ
4. ● Ⓖ Ⓗ Ⓙ
5. Ⓐ Ⓑ ● Ⓓ
6. Ⓕ Ⓖ Ⓗ ●
7. Ⓐ Ⓑ Ⓒ ●
8. Ⓕ ● Ⓗ Ⓙ

Section B

9. Ⓐ Ⓑ Ⓒ ●
10. Ⓕ Ⓖ Ⓗ ●
11. Ⓐ ● Ⓒ Ⓓ
12. ● Ⓖ Ⓗ Ⓙ
13. ● Ⓑ Ⓒ Ⓓ

Section C

14. Ⓕ ● Ⓗ Ⓙ
15. Ⓐ ● Ⓒ Ⓓ
16. Ⓕ Ⓖ ● Ⓙ
17. ● Ⓑ Ⓒ Ⓓ
18. Ⓕ Ⓖ Ⓗ ●

Post-test A

1. ● Ⓑ Ⓒ Ⓓ
2. Ⓕ Ⓖ ● Ⓙ
3. Ⓐ Ⓑ Ⓒ ●
4. ● Ⓖ Ⓗ Ⓙ
5. Ⓐ Ⓑ ● Ⓓ
6. Ⓕ ● Ⓗ Ⓙ
7. Ⓐ ● Ⓒ Ⓓ
8. Ⓕ Ⓖ Ⓗ ●
9. Ⓐ Ⓑ ● Ⓓ
10. Ⓕ ● Ⓗ Ⓙ
11. Ⓐ Ⓑ Ⓒ ●
12. ● Ⓖ Ⓗ Ⓙ
13. ● Ⓑ Ⓒ Ⓓ
14. Ⓕ Ⓖ ● Ⓙ
15. Ⓐ ● Ⓒ Ⓓ
16. Ⓕ Ⓖ Ⓗ ●
17. Ⓐ Ⓑ ● Ⓓ
18. ● Ⓖ Ⓗ Ⓙ

Post-test B

1. Ⓐ Ⓑ ● Ⓓ
2. Ⓕ Ⓖ Ⓗ ●
3. Ⓐ Ⓑ Ⓒ Ⓓ
4. Ⓕ Ⓖ ● Ⓙ
5. Ⓐ Ⓑ Ⓒ ●
6. ● Ⓖ Ⓗ Ⓙ
7. ● Ⓑ Ⓒ Ⓓ
8. Ⓕ ● Ⓗ Ⓙ
9. ● Ⓑ Ⓒ Ⓓ
10. Ⓕ Ⓖ ● Ⓙ
11. Ⓐ Ⓑ ● Ⓓ
12. Ⓕ Ⓖ Ⓗ ●
13. Ⓐ ● Ⓒ Ⓓ
14. ● Ⓖ Ⓗ Ⓙ
15. Ⓐ Ⓑ Ⓒ ●
16. Ⓕ ● Ⓗ Ⓙ
17. Ⓐ ● Ⓒ Ⓓ
18. Ⓕ Ⓖ ● Ⓙ

Pretest ■

Post-test A ▲

Post-test B ◆

Correlation

For help with test items	Use		
1–8	Section **A**	Factors and Multiples	
9–13	Section **B**	Introduction to Fractions	
14–18	Section **C**	Fractions, Mixed Numbers, and Decimals	

Note: Test item numbers on all tests also correspond to skill numbers. For example, item 4 on each test corresponds to Skill 4.

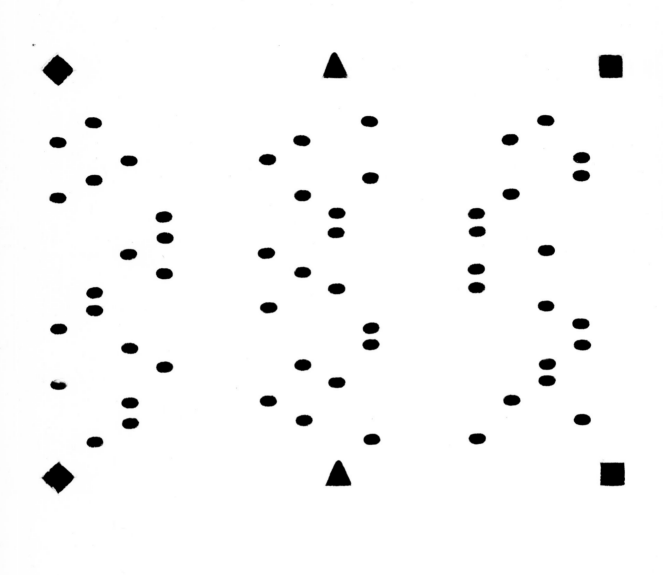